Dear Ross

Evelyn O'Rourke is a broadcaster and journalist from Dublin. After studying Drama and English at Trinity College, she joined RTÉ where she has presented and reported on a wide range of radio and TV programmes in both Irish and English.

Evelyn joined *The Gerry Ryan Show* on 2fm in 2002 where she worked as Gerry's reporter for eight years. In 2010 she was diagnosed with breast cancer while pregnant with her second child. After successful treatment, she returned to work at RTÉ Radio 1.

Evelyn is married to John McMahon and they have two sons, Oisín and Ross. She loves reading, writing, talking and sleep. Not always in that order.

You can follow her on twitter at @evelyn_orourke and find more information on www.evelynorourke.ie.

Dear Ross is her first book.

DEAR ROSS

Evelyn O'Rourke

HACHETTE
BOOKS
IRELAND

First published in 2014 by Hachette Books Ireland

A CIP catalogue record for this title is available from the British Library

ISBN 978 1444 789 843

Typeset in Bembo Book Std by Bookends Publishing Services
Printed and bound by CPI Group (UK) Ltd, Croydon, CR0 4YY

Hachette Books Ireland policy is to use papers that are natural, renewable
and recyclable products and made from wood grown in sustainable forests.
The logging and manufacturing processes are expected to conform to the
environmental regulations of the country of origin.

Hachette Books Ireland
8 Castlecourt Centre
Castleknock
Dublin 15, Ireland

A division of Hachette UK Ltd
338 Euston Road
London NW1 3BH

www.hachette.ie

To Oisín, Ross and John
my everything

Prologue

Dear Ross,

You have just fallen asleep in my arms.

I put you in the cot an hour ago but you started roaring, as you weren't a bit happy about being put to bed, so eventually I gave in, picked you up and sat in the rocking chair in darkness, rubbing your back gently until you finally dropped off to sleep snuggled in my arms.

And as we sat there, some memories from the last two years flashed into my mind and I got that shiver down my spine. For a time I had it hourly but in the last six months it's hardly happened at all. When it does, though, I'm instantly transported back to that week.

The week that ricocheted from sheer joy to sheer terror in the space of a few days. I kiss your head in gratitude because, thankfully, the shiver down my spine is becoming a stranger to me now.

For some time, I have been thinking about writing to you about the beginning of your life – the earliest chapters of a life that I hope will be exciting, fulfilling, thrilling and fascinating. But your start was tough, and that's what I want to talk to you about. You and I had to survive a horrendous ordeal before we could meet and live a normal life.

As you approach your second birthday, that is exactly what life is now: normal. You hate getting dressed and wriggle uncontrollably while I try to change you. You love bananas and hate beef stew. You have eleven and a half teeth and the others are coming fast. You love having your brother, Oisín, playing around you and hate it when he wanders off. You hate being strapped into the car seat and love chewing your socks. You love going out for a walk and complain loudly if I stop the buggy for more than a minute.

In other words, you're normal. Our life is normal. Finally, we have reached the normality I dreamt about when the horror of that week in June 2010 gripped me.

I'm going to tell you the story of an ordinary life that was suddenly and shockingly thrown into a nightmare and how, with all the love, support, kindness and luck in the world, that life has returned to normal.

People ask me all the time how I coped with the situation we were landed in and I usually smile and say

I had fantastic family, friends and medical teams who guided me along every step of the way, which is true. But, unlike most patients, I had a secret weapon. I had a tiny beating heart in my womb that willed me on.

Yours, my love.

My baby, Ross. You were my heart for a time, so that is why I say that this is not just *my* story. It's *our* story. A mother and a son.

But while your story began just weeks after you were conceived, for mine we have to go back a little further, to 20 November 2009, just before everything changed for ever.

All my love,

Mama

Chapter 1

Two Becomes Three

On New Year's Eve in 2009, after much thought, deliberation and planning, I hit on a highly original idea: let's just stay at home! Every other year, having ignored the idea of celebrating for days beforehand, I would then frantically spend the afternoon on the phone to friends, trying to make elaborate last-minute plans for the evening, but that year was different. That year I didn't want to be anywhere except in our own home because we had a baby to hug when the clocks struck twelve. Finally, after so many years, we had our first baby in our arms. Our son Oisín was a whole three weeks old, and as we rang in the new year, I thought my heart would explode with happiness.

Holding Oisín tightly during the countdown to midnight, I looked at my husband, John, and he winked back at me and we just knew 2010 was going to be a wonderful year for us. We had a beautiful baby boy and I was going to be on maternity leave for the next few months to enjoy every minute. Life was sweet.

When I think back now, all I can do is shake my head. What fools we were. How could we sit there cocooned in our little world, and not realise that we would soon be swept away in a storm of fear, confusion and panic? On that New Year's Eve, 2010 promised so much and now, it was the speed with which everything fell into turmoil that shocks me most. One minute I was basking in the glow of being a new mum and the next I was marching down hospital corridors, terror in my heart, the ground seeming to crack under my every step.

I suppose this story really begins a few weeks before that New Year's Eve, when I started my maternity leave. I left my desk in RTÉ on Friday, 20 November 2009, at lunchtime midday and headed off for a goodbye lunch with my team and as I left the office that day in 2009, I had no idea that, after nearly eight years working as the reporter on *The Gerry Ryan Show*, it had been the final time I would sit at that desk.

On that November day, I was so happy. I was heavily pregnant with my first baby and was heading out the door to start my maternity leave. My colleagues were determined to send me off in style: I'd spotted bulging gift bags under desks, so I guessed they had organised some presents for me. That I remember, but it's difficult to recall any more details of that day with any certainty. I have replayed it over and over in my mind so many times that I'm sure I've strayed from what actually happened. Were my colleagues really just sitting calmly at their desks, making arrangements for the following week's programmes before we headed off for lunch? Was Gerry just sitting in his corner desk as normal, chatting away on his phone? How could I have had no clue to let me know that this would be the last time I would see that familiar scene after nearly eight years of it being my daily life?

Before I left that November day I tidied away a couple of things, leaving some personal bits and pieces in my drawers for my return. I had been working in radio for many years and always loved being at the heart of the action in the station. I had joined RTÉ back in 1998 as a researcher and had quickly stepped into reporting and presenting, both of which I adored. As I was checking that my battered stapler still actually stapled, I suddenly realised that, from today, I would be at home. I would be 'a listener'. Relegated to the sidelines. In fact, scratch that, I was *choosing* the sidelines. My new life as a mother would take over from the daily diet of newspaper reading, programme meetings and broadcasting challenges that had filled my working life for years. That was going to be very strange but as John had just been appointed Head of

2fm a few weeks earlier, at least I would have some idea of what was going on in work during my confinement. My plan then was to have the baby, head back to work the following year and life would continue as normal.

Normal. I was normal then. I was heading off to start my maternity leave like any other first-time mother. I was so excited because leaving that day meant that the moment I would meet my new baby was getting closer and closer, but along with that excitement, I could feel butterflies in my stomach. I knew how to be a wife, daughter, sister, daughter-in-law, aunt and, yes, a broadcaster but at that moment, tidying my desk, I did not have the first idea how to be a mother. I was closely involved with my nephews and nieces but in fairness, I had generally only dealt with them after a full night's sleep. How would John and I cope with a bambino that was going to be ours and ours alone? Like a lot of people, I get cranky when I'm tired, and while I knew that having a tiny baby was going to be an amazing experience, I wasn't convinced that I would cope elegantly or gracefully with nightmarish-sounding three a.m. feeds. John and I used to coo at the idea of a tiny person arriving into our world, but sitting at my desk that day, I felt a surge of uncertainty.

My office was familiar and I knew how that world operated, but the new job I'd applied for? The mama bit? Gulp.

My thoughts were interrupted when one of the team called me. It was time to go and they hustled me out of the door for lunch. I left my doubts in a drawer in my desk for another day.

As we made our way into town, we were talking about that morning's programme and how emotional it had been for me. I had been in the studio on-air live with Gerry, and as he was signing off at the end of the programme I had started to head out of the studio but he had called me back. As it was a minute past twelve, the show had officially ended but he apologised to the newsreader and turned to me. Out of the blue, he made a beautiful speech on-air wishing myself and John well with the new baby and thanking me for all my hard work on the show. I was moved to tears. It was an utterly unexpected and very sweet tribute. Sitting there, I suddenly had flashbacks to when I'd first started working with him. Back in the summer of 2002, I'd had a phone call inviting me to try out as a reporter on the show for a couple of months. I'd liked Gerry and, thankfully, he'd seemed to like me, so I had been on the show ever since. Back to today's show, though: I was so stunned by what he'd said that I just thanked him and sat there smiling. He gave me a wink and I headed out again. I knew I would passionately miss the show and his studio, CC3, where I had spent so many happy hours chatting on-air about every topic under the sun. Incredibly, that was to be our final broadcast together.

The image I have of him sitting there, headphones wrapped around his head, newspapers in piles on his desk and on the floor, was so familiar that I'm shocked even now that that was the last time I was on-air with him.

That day, I waddled out of the studio and back up to the office where the team and I got ready to head into town. As I think about us packing up our things and making our way out to the front of the radio centre, I have a picture in my head that I cannot shake: a pregnant woman is standing on the steps of the radio centre, waiting with friends for a cab in the winter sunshine. She is so happy and excited, more content than she ever thought possible, and chatting enthusiastically to her colleagues. When it arrives she walks down the steps and looks back one more time at the radio centre, then gets into the car.

That picture haunts me. It shocks me that my life, which was so happy, so secure, so content, was about to be overturned and thrown into turmoil.

I had the goodbye lunch with my colleagues and we had such fun swapping pregnancy advice and horror labour stories that lunch turned into dinner, and I danced until midnight before the bump and I finally gave up and went home.

Next morning, I packed away my dancing shoes and checked my first job on the maternity-leave to-do list. Oh, yes: have a baby. Just under two weeks to go until that particular job had to be handled. Hmm …

I am usually quite adept at getting John to do some of my tougher chores, but this time there was no outsourcing. The birth was approaching and I had to remain calm, but even the mantra that millions and millions of women all over the world had given birth successfully for centuries was cold comfort. I am, clearly, not the bravest of souls. A baby was coming and I, terrified of needles, blood and pain, had to deal with whatever came with it.

Some days later, on 1 December, John and I visited my obstetrician. She confirmed to us, yet again, that while the baby was doing really well it was not yet engaged properly. She was concerned that if things didn't improve, we might be looking at a Christmas induction!

She asked me gently how I felt about having a Caesarean section, and we said that of course we wanted a straightforward delivery so whatever the doctor considered the best course of action was fine by us. So, how would we feel about a C-section the following day? she asked. Fine, we agreed, if that would be best for the baby, but inside I was churning. A baby. Tomorrow?

We went home reeling at the idea that we were going to be parents in less than twenty-four hours. We talked about the jobs that needed doing before the baby came. Luckily, we seemed to have most of them sorted. In fact, we were well organised apart from one small issue: the baby's name. We had chosen – well, *I* had chosen – not to find out the sex of the baby beforehand and had filled the previous several months with passionate discussions about names. Suddenly, tomorrow, we would have to pick one. Who was the stranger who was about to arrive into our lives? How could they be on their way when we didn't even have a name for them? It was bizarre.

The next day we checked into the hospital and at four sixteen p.m. precisely our gorgeous, healthy baby was born. Our doctor said, 'It's a little man,' and we both broke down, weeping with joy.

After years of trying to have a baby, he was finally here. He was seven pounds and two ounces, a perfect, crumpled little scrap of a thing, and we adored him. I remember a nurse laying him on my chest and John was wrapped around the two of us and we just wept. 'You're here, you're here,' I kept whispering to our tiny boy. 'You're finally here and we love you so much.' The three of us were cuddled together and the rest of the world just faded away. The pregnancy was over, no more dreary symptoms or prenatal stuff, the baby had arrived, and our life as a family could begin. 'Hooray, little man,' I remember murmuring to him.

After a few minutes, the nurses wheeled me off to Recovery and John took the baby upstairs. As he was leaving, he mouthed at me, 'Oisín?'

I nodded. Yes. I think so. It was a beautiful name and we both loved it. Oisín Brian McMahon. As I lay on my bed in Recovery, a sense of utter contentment began to spread through me, filling me up, pumping around my body – as vital now to me as the blood in my veins. A while later, when I was wheeled up to the ward, I remember seeing John waiting for me with our son in his arms. I remember looking at them both and thinking, This is going to be OK. I don't think we can screw it up too badly.

It was fantastic.

Family and friends rushed in that evening to be introduced to Oisín, and it was wonderful to watch his grandparents, aunts and uncles hold him and welcome him into the world.

After a few days, we were discharged and went home, a little nervous with the new bundle but filled with excitement about our future together as a family. It was heading towards Christmas and those weeks after I had Oisín were the happiest in my life. Christmas itself was a blur of feeds, nappies and visitors, and I loved every minute of it. Then on Tuesday, 5 January, John returned to work and slowly life acquired a rhythm, with a mother-and-baby routine. My mother, Peigí, who is also my next-door neighbour, was a daily visitor, as were my sister, Kim, and John's parents, Brian and Margaret.

Once I had finally worked out how the buggy actually clicked into place, Oisín and I headed out into the world. I loved being with him so much that even those dreaded night feeds could not dent my enthusiasm for this new person in my life. John's father, Brian, had carved a magnificent cradle for Oisín and it was at the end of the bed in our room. I was never more than a few feet away from him in those early weeks. The minute he stirred in the mornings I would be hanging over the edge of the cradle soothing him, unable to resist the temptation to pick him up and cuddle him. I would feed him, change him and then we would go downstairs and make plans for the day. It was a dream. We went for walks in the park, dropped in for coffee to anyone who would have us, and I was always talking to him, telling him about his cousins and filling him in on the neighbourhood. Every evening John would bound in the door from work, eager to hug him and hear about our day. Life was blissful. One day, on my way to meet my pal Elayne for a playdate, I remember driving, with Oisín in the back of the car, and thinking, Are you allowed to be this happy?

I find that bizarre now. Why did that thought occur to me? Why was there any doubt?

Now I wince when I see pictures from that time.

It hurts me to see how naïve we were then, so innocent. But I'm so grateful for those precious carefree months. John and I were in love with each other and our gorgeous son, and we had no idea that a wrecking ball was coming in our direction.

It all began with a small, angry-looking spot.

Chapter 2

First Sign of Trouble

After Oisín was born we assumed that we would have to wait a long time again for our second, if we were so lucky as to have a second, so we decided to enjoy life with the three of us. By the time he was five months old, Oisín was starting to sleep through the night so we decided to book a holiday to the Canaries. The day we were due to fly out, the infamous Icelandic volcano with the unpronounceable name – Eyjafjallajökull – erupted and all flights were grounded. We came home from the airport sorely disappointed but we were assured that we could rebook and decided to try again in a few weeks' time.

For now, though, I was looking forward to a fun,

relaxed summer. I had a long list of places I wanted to visit with the baby, including an exhaustive list of parks and gardens I had studiously researched on the web. I was lucky to have lots of friends and colleagues I wanted to catch up with so every week I would plan my mother-and-baby sessions for the mornings and meet up with grannies or pals in the afternoons. It was a charmed life.

One morning, near the end of April, I was getting dressed when I noticed something on my breast.

It looked like an angry spot, like the kind an unlucky teenager would have on their chin, and it was sitting next to the nipple on my right breast. Hmm … I thought. I felt around the breast but couldn't detect anything like a lump so I decided to keep an eye on it. I wasn't particularly bothered by it so I put it out of my mind and finished dressing.

To be honest, at that time I was more concerned about the baby's feeds and introducing him to solids than the spot on my breast, and any vague worry I might have had about it soon faded completely from my mind.

A few days later, on Friday, 30 April 2010, my work life was about to shatter in the saddest way possible. That date is engraved on my heart as it is our wedding anniversary but it was about to take on even more significance for us. On that day in 2010, our fifth anniversary, my friend Gerry Ryan died. It was one of the bleakest days of my life.

Just after lunchtime that day, Oisín and I were in my sister Kim's house when John rang. I answered the mobile awkwardly while balancing the baby and launching into some boring description of my day. Uncharacteristically, he cut me off.

'Where are you?' he barked.

'At Kim's.'

'What are you doing?'

'Eh … feeding the baby.'

'Give the baby to Kim right now. I need to talk to you.'

'Oh, OK.' Shuffle, shuffle, as I waved at Kim and passed Oisín over to her. She brought him into the sitting room to continue with his bottle.

'What is it?' I asked.

'Evelyn, I have terrible news. Gerry's dead.'

'I'm sorry – what do you mean, Gerry's dead?'

'Gerry. Gerry Ryan is dead. Mike [his brother] has just told me. I have to go now and talk to people so stay with Kim and I'll be back in touch.'

'John, are you sure you've got this right? He was on-air yesterday – how can he be dead?'

'Ev, I'm so sorry but it's definitely true and I need you not to talk to anyone else now until you hear back from me. I'll keep in touch, sweetheart, and give the baby a kiss.'

I slowly hung up and turned to Kim, who was staring at me from the couch. She was looking at me in shock.

'Gerry's dead, Kim,' I gasped. 'Jesus Christ, John says that Gerry's dead. Gerry Ryan is dead.' I felt a wave of nausea and tears formed in my eyes.

I remember standing there, holding on to the worktop and starting to shake a little. Kim came over to me and I relayed the conversation to her again and again as I struggled to let it sink in.

And then my phone beeped with a message from a journalist pal in a different radio station, asking me politely to give him a ring as he'd just heard a mad rumour about Gerry and wanted to discuss it with me. When I read that message, I knew it was true. Word was spreading like wildfire in Dublin, and as the phone beeped with similar messages, I collapsed in a heap sobbing. Gerry was dead and all I could do was cry.

You see, like hundreds of thousands of people, I loved Gerry Ryan. I loved the on-air Gerry Ryan. The broadcasting genius. The messer. The brat. The troublemaker. The entertainer. The know-it-all. The wise elder. All of his on-air roles. And off-air, in real life, I loved the father figure in the office. I loved that he could make me collapse laughing ten seconds after he arrived into the office. I loved his kindness to us, his team, his loyalty to us, and his unwavering support and help to me whenever I looked to him for advice or guidance on work matters. Also, I loved the way he adored his listeners. The *Gerry Ryan Show* listeners. As I stood in my sister's house reeling at the news of his death, I thought of them. They would be devastated by his death. Back in that dark afternoon, knowing he was gone, so many memories of times spent on the show ran through my mind but, more than anything, I was struck by how his listeners would feel. They had turned on his programme each morning at nine for more than twenty years and his death would leave a terrible gap for them. I slumped on the sofa, with my buzzing phone in my hand.

Eventually John rang again. I told him that I was feeling shocked and scared and he told me that I needed to come into the radio centre and be with my radio family. He was right. I wanted to be nowhere else: I had spent so many great days with my friends in that building. Eight years ago, I had started working with Gerry when I was young, free and single, and during my time on the show, I had got engaged, married and headed off to have a baby. All through these huge life events, Gerry and the team had been there in the background, supporting me, happy to help on any issue as I stumbled my way through the decisions that come with adult life.

Today I needed to be back with them, so I got Oisín's stuff organised, packed him into the car and we drove in to RTÉ. As soon as I had parked and was hauling the buggy out of the car, people came to greet us. As I wheeled Oisín inside, others descended on us, welcoming us with tears and hugs. I remember getting the buggy into the office and found everyone gathering in the 2fm area. John was running around, managing the fallout from the news, and my colleagues were stumbling through the day. We had never experienced anything like this before. I doubt anyone in RTÉ had.

I was back at my old desk but everything had changed since the November day when I had gone off on maternity leave, not least the beautiful baby in the buggy parked beside me. At around tea time I was called into John's office where he was standing with a group of senior colleagues. He looked me straight in the eye and said he had a question for me. They had decided that I should present the tribute programme the next morning if I was up for it. Was I?

I was stunned, overwhelmed, soggy from all the crying, and was about to say no, I couldn't do it, I just wasn't up to it, when I stopped myself. I know this show, I thought. I love this audience, and I know how Gerry would want this show to go so I'm going to say yes. I agreed to front it with my good pal Brenda Donohue in the studio beside me for the duration.

We had to decide what to do on the show and as we made plans to get clips of Gerry's best moments (there were too many), to contact some of our favourite guests and to pick the music we all started to put a show together. Of course, we couldn't contemplate doing a show for Gerry without inviting his favourite band, U2, to contribute. We had no idea where in the world they were but eventually we got the call that Bono and the Edge would talk to us. They were in America, shocked at the news that Gerry had died. The deal was that they would talk to us at midnight, Irish time, for a pre-recorded interview. It was a huge relief to line them up: Gerry loved U2. He thought of the radio show as his own rock band and always enjoyed talking to Bono and the Edge about their latest escapades, so it was fitting that they featured on the programme.

We kept working on our running orders and then after we handed Oisín over to my brother Colm for an emergency sleepover, John and I – wearing a clean shirt and dress respectively – headed over to RTÉ TV at about nine p.m. Arriving into the *Late Late Show* green room was surreal. The atmosphere was very emotionally charged. We sat in the audience as Ryan Tubridy spoke to friends and colleagues about the shocking loss we'd suffered just that day. When it came to my turn, I spoke about the text Gerry had sent me the night Oisín was born, 'Welcome to my world', which summed him up completely. I said that with Gerry it had always been about family and his was at the centre of his life.

The rest of the show passed in a blur. We went backstage and there were more tears. Then John and I returned to the radio centre, which was now quiet and still. We waited in a little studio in 2fm for U2 to ring through. There was nothing we could do but sit there and count the minutes. After the turmoil of the day, it was strange to sit in the quiet, waiting for a phone call from two of the biggest names in the world of music. On any other day I would have had butterflies in my stomach but that night I just wanted to make sure we got what we needed. The call came at around midnight, as agreed, and both Bono and the Edge paid moving tributes to Gerry. Bono wished him goodnight in the poetic way that only he can. Gerry would have loved it.

After we had finished the interview, Bono and the Edge wanted to go on talking about Gerry. We all discussed how tragic the news was and they wished us luck for the morning's programme. Recording done, we turned off the lights in the studio and went home to try to get some sleep.

Chapter 3

Remembering

The next day was a Saturday, and a bank-holiday Saturday at that. Normally that would mean a quiet RTÉ radio centre, but that day was different. A group of us who had worked with Gerry for years gathered early in the studios and ploughed through the newspapers, which were full of pictures and stories from Gerry's long career. Not every photo was flattering. He had had many dodgy hairstyles over the years and the papers had dug out pictures from the archives, which made us laugh.

Ten minutes before we went on air, Brenda Donohue, Alice O'Sullivan – who was Gerry's producer at that time – and I went downstairs to prepare for the show as we had all done so often in the past. We were old friends who had met on Gerry's show and now, after all those years working with him, we found ourselves making our way downstairs to *his* studio, *his* chair and *his* mic.

It was terrible.

And then we were on-air. We opened the Ryan-line, invited listeners to ring us and the calls came flooding in. Relief washed over me.

A few moments stand out for me from that programme, like the man ringing in to tell us he was a travelling salesman who spent many hours trapped in his car and that Gerry had been his side passenger for many years. He asked us what he was supposed to do now that his wingman was gone.

Lavinia Kerwick was another memorable caller. She was the person Gerry had credited with placing his show firmly into the spotlight and convincing people to take it seriously. As a young woman, Lavinia had been raped by an ex-boyfriend and had waived her right to anonymity to speak to Gerry about the attack and the court case surrounding it. That interview had caused shockwaves at the time. Now she was back to mourn him and talked to us about how Gerry had helped her.

We could have stayed on all day, but at five to twelve Alice said quietly into my headphones, 'Start winding it down now.'

And suddenly it hit me. This was goodbye.

I shakily thanked all our guests and our listeners, then

said goodbye to Gerry directly. I told him we loved him, and at that my voice broke.

John appeared out of somewhere and guided me up the stairs. All I could see were queues and queues of people milling around the radio-centre reception area.

Earlier in the show, we had announced that there would be a book of condolence for people to sign, and they had been turning up all morning, standing patiently in line to add their names. I stood in the foyer in awe – the weather was so dreadful yet still people came.

I saw mothers dragging buggies out of cars and getting soaked. I saw small knots of people in raincoats, wielding umbrellas and making their way through the sheets of rain just to come in and sign the book. I spoke to one man who had risen early that morning in Cork and clambered onto a bus to Dublin to sign the book. Another woman had arrived in Busáras never having been to Dublin before and had asked a taxi driver to guide her to RTÉ. He had driven her to Donnybrook and they had waited in the rain together to sign the book before he drove her back to her bus without charging her a penny. It was an extraordinary sight and I stood there for a long time watching those people – it was an experience I will always remember vividly.

We crawled through the weekend, and the phone calls became a blur. By Monday lunchtime, a decision had been taken and John rang to say that there would be a show on Tuesday morning. It would be kept simple, letting the listeners talk and playing some of Gerry's best bits from over the years. Again I was invited to sit in the presenter's seat, with Brenda beside me, and I gladly accepted. On Tuesday morning at eight fifty-five, Brenda and I were back in Gerry's studio, asking the listeners to call us one more time.

Everyone gathered again on Wednesday morning, when the funeral took place at St John the Baptist Church in Clontarf. The ceremony was conducted by Father Michael Collins. Both he and Gerry's family spoke movingly about their love for him. Father Brian D'Arcy's eulogy also struck a chord with many.

Down at the back of the church, a little wooden box had been erected as a mini radio studio for Colm Hayes and Mark Little, who were anchoring the service, which was broadcast live on 2fm. At first, the idea of broadcasting it had seemed bizarre but we discovered that it wouldn't be a first for 2fm because a mass had been broadcast on the station before, if a long time ago. Back in 1979 John Paul II had held a youth mass in Galway, which the new Radio 2 had broadcast, but since then, the station had put out very little religion. When it was decided to allow coverage of Gerry's funeral, John laughed as he reckoned Gerry would have enjoyed the irony of being responsible for a slice of religion on the airwaves.

As I made my way out of the church car park, many women came up to me to say hello and to tell me how much they had appreciated the tribute shows, which was lovely.

Later, on the news, I saw a woman who had been interviewed as she stood outside the church with her double buggy. She told the reporter that she was a single parent with two small babies and that Gerry had been her lifeline. She had turned him on every single morning and he had helped her through her day. She was devastated at his death.

I knew how she felt: his show, both on- and off-air, had been the centre of my own world for years and now, suddenly, it was over.

Chapter 4

Rollercoasters

Two weeks later, having rebooked our holiday, John, Oisín and I flew to the Canaries for a badly needed week's break. It was great to get away from the sadness, but reality wasn't very far away because of the many phone calls John was fielding as he and his colleagues worked out the next piece in the 2fm jigsaw. His phone had rung endlessly on the dreadful day when Gerry had died and it had barely paused since. I knew that John's thoughts were at home as he tried to figure out what to do next, but I was determined for him to enjoy parts of the holiday too. With everything up in the air at work, who knew when we would next get a chance to be away together on our own? We spent hours by the pool, reading and talking. Often when John's phone rang he would head off with the buggy, wheeling Oisín around the grounds, phone clamped to his ear. The joys of being away with a small baby is that Ois was quite happy to be in his buggy while we soaked up the sun, and in the evening we would wrap him up warmly and go to a quiet local restaurant as he slept under his layers.

Despite the ringing phone, we had some lovely times on that holiday, and the photos of the three of us relaxing in the warm sunshine hold a special place in my heart.

Within days of our return home, though, our little world was to be shattered and that calm, normal (ish!) holiday will always be a precious memory for me.

With all the turmoil of the previous three weeks, I had forgotten my niggling worry about my breast, but on the last night of our holiday I noticed that the pimple was still there. It started to nag at me again. I mentioned it to John, who said I should go to the doctor as soon as we got home and get it checked out.

The next day, back at home, I rang the Women's Health Clinic in Leopardstown and made an appointment to see Dr Laura Barker that afternoon. I rang John's parents, Margaret and Brian, and asked them to mind Oisín as I had to go out for a while. I decided not to tell them where I was going because I wasn't particularly concerned.

When I arrived for my appointment, Dr Barker examined me and said that the spot could be an infection so she was going to prescribe an antibiotic for me. However, she went on to say that she didn't like the look of it – no woman should have anything at all on their breast for any length of time – so she was going to make an appointment for me with Mr Denis Evoy, a surgeon and breast cancer expert in St Vincent's Hospital. As she was making the appointment for the following week, I sat there rigid with shock. This was the very first time that I had ever heard the term 'cancer' in relation to me and it hadn't entered my head that this bloody pimple thing could be anything so sinister. I tried desperately to remember when I had first spotted it. How long had it been there? I estimated four weeks and comforted myself with the thought that nothing too bad could have happened in such a short time.

Dr Barker told me to take the antibiotic and hopefully the spot would disappear but I should keep an eye on it. If there was no change after a week I should see Mr Denis Evoy.

Interestingly, one of the reasons she was wary about the pimple was that it didn't hurt when she touched it. She could tweak it and pinch it and there was no pain. She told me that if it was a regular infection it should be sore to manipulate. I was slowly to learn over the next few months that one of the most evil characteristics of cancer is that often the symptoms don't hurt, which is why some people are diagnosed with very advanced conditions. How often have you heard of someone being diagnosed with cancer and told they had weeks to live when they had been feeling fine? That makes me so angry – and is another reason why I hate the disease. You can get a simple paper cut and be in pain, or you can develop cancer and not be the slightest bit aware that it's taking over your body.

I was reeling when I left the doctor's surgery. I returned to John's parents' house and picked up Oisín but said nothing to them – I had no idea what I could say and didn't want to upset anyone unnecessarily. Surely it was just a stupid infection and I would have to cancel the appointment with that nice man Denis Evoy.

I spent the week staring at the pimple and by the end I was convinced that it had decreased a little in size. I pestered John, asking him to compare it to last night and how it had looked that morning. After a week, though, even I had to concede that it hadn't changed in size, so the following Tuesday I headed towards St Vincent's with the baby. John cycled down from RTÉ to meet me there.

At first I was fine. Then I started to get a little upset in the waiting room. What if …? flashed into my mind. As I checked in with Kitty, Denis' wife and secretary, she offered to mind Oisín for me when the man himself appeared. He was much younger and friendlier than I'd expected. He was relaxed and warm, and told us that Oisín was more than welcome in the surgery during my appointment so we wheeled him in.

Denis took a look at the pimple and went on to tell us

that he wanted to investigate further. He explained to us that he was going to order all the biopsies and blood tests so that we knew exactly what we were dealing with but meanwhile he was recommending that I should plan to have it removed fairly quickly anyway. No major alarm bells went off for me at that point though, so I had a quick chat with myself and decided that it must be just a cyst. I relaxed a little – after all, any woman who has gone through pregnancy gets used to bumps and lumps appearing and disappearing from her body and this spot just seemed to be another one of those mysterious things. I vaguely knew that cyst is a term to describe a fluid-filled sac which is usually not cancerous, so I decided there and then that my spot would turn out to be a boring cyst. I'd heard enough. I did not really know the finer points of what a cyst was but I was sure it was going to turn out to be one: it would be removed and we could get on with our lives. I went back to Kitty to make arrangements and whispered to her that I thought it looked like everything was going to be fine. We made appointments for the following week and John headed back to work. Oisín and I went home. We still hadn't told anyone what was happening at that point, so I decided to mention it to my sister, Kim. I didn't want to upset my mum, and Kim is very practical and calm about these things. I met up with her, outlined the situation and then we moved on to other topics. She was, of course, much relieved that everything was looking OK, so I got on with my day-to-day life, which at that time coincidentally involved organising my (ahem, twentieth anniversary of leaving) school reunion.

I had been in an all-Irish secondary school in Stillorgan, Dublin, with a young man called Dara Ó Briain, and we had kept in touch over the years. I had been in the girls' school, Coláiste Íosagáin, and he had been in the boys' school, Coláiste Eoin. All these years later, a lot of our school friends were still in contact so we had been kicking around the idea of a reunion. Dara, who is now a comedian and TV presenter, was planning a string of dates in Vicar Street that summer, so we decided that one June evening we should book out a section of the audience, invite our old classmates and have a party there afterwards.

He and I had first discussed this idea back in January when John and I had been to see his show, and in the months since then I had been on Facebook, email and old-fashioned snail mail trying to enlist as many as I could find of our former 120 schoolmates to come to the reunion. I had been doing well, ringing old friends and family and had really put my heart and soul into ensuring that it was going to be the best reunion we could offer. I was determined to get through the lists of names, and after I'd seen Denis I returned to my part-time maternity-leave job of tracking down old friends. It was a terrific distraction.

The following week I was called in for the first of the tests and biopsies but neither John nor I was overly concerned about the results. My biopsy was carried out by Dr Ann O'Doherty who is a consultant radiologist and the clinical lead at BreastCheck in St Vincent's. Ann is a fireball of energy and warmth and I liked her immediately. She works with a great team including Mary Kieran, who was the first breast-care nurse I met. Mary was calm and reassuring as she guided me through everything, but both John and I were stupidly calm too as we faced into this unknown world. Why were we so unconcerned? Well, we were both busy with Oisín, the reunion and, of course, the fallout from Gerry's death, which was very much occupying John's mind. When I look back to that time now, I find it hard to believe that we had no real sense of the impending earthquake that was due to erupt in our lives. I remember the first day I met Mary and being confused that I had to even talk to a breast-care nurse. It definitely seemed odd to me that I was in that 'category' when we had no tangible evidence of any problem, but I was still in the maternity world where chatting to complete strangers about my breasts was a common occurrence. Maybe we were in denial but I really do not think we had any clue. I was convinced that it was going to be a cyst or something mildly troubling but nothing major. I went along with the tests and the appointments because I have a strong obedience streak, rather than because I believed that something sinister was happening inside me that needed to be investigated.

The following weekend was the June bank holiday, and

I was looking forward to a few quiet days with John and the baby. John and I had not seen a lot of each other lately because as Head of 2fm, negotiations for a replacement for Gerry were so intense at this stage that I felt like our kitchen was a 2fm outpost.

On Sunday night, I was feeling a little stuffed up so decided to take some flu medicine. Tired and standing in our bathroom, I was about to swallow it when I checked the fact sheet, something I rarely do. It carried a stark warning that if you were pregnant you should under no circumstances take the tablets. It was printed three different times in bold. Like anyone else, I could ignore that kind of warning once. By the second time, I was mildly irritated, and by the third I was so annoyed that I told John the advice sheet was determined I should do a pregnancy test. John said he thought that there was an old testing kit in my bedside locker and I should do the test just to satisfy myself that I was, of course, not pregnant.

I marched back into the bedroom. John dug out the test, chucked it across the room to me and promptly snuggled back under the duvet. Of course, when I checked *that* packaging, it told me that it was best to do the test first thing in the morning. 'Fine,' I snapped at the box. 'I'll do it first thing tomorrow, bank-holiday Monday morning, and conclusively prove to you that I am not pregnant.'

I went to bed.

Next morning, I crawled out of the bed, grabbed the

stupid test stick, marched into the bathroom and did the test. You have to wait a minute or two for the result to appear so I yawningly put the stick down to brush my teeth or something equally exciting to fill the gap.

Things did not go exactly to plan. I had hardly let go of the stick when the blue line emerged.

Actually, it's untrue to say it emerged. It *exploded* onto the stick. It was the strongest, thickest, bluest line ever, and my heart was suddenly thumping loudly. I had done the test to confirm that I was not pregnant and there I was with the shiniest blue line in the world. I blinked several times. How could I be pregnant? Oisín was just six months old so how could that have happened? I sat down heavily on the side of the bath and felt a surge of, first, excitement, then crippling fear.

What if the test was faulty and had given me a horrible false reading? I was sitting on the edge of the bath clutching that stick and I could hardly believe it. After years of trying to have children, there was no way we were going to be lucky enough to have a second baby so easily and quickly, was there?

I called out to John, who had Oisín lying beside him. He said afterwards that he had suddenly got a weird feeling because I had been banging around in the bathroom, making lots of noise, and then suddenly I had gone very, very quiet. Suspiciously quiet.

I called out quietly and, bizarrely, politely, 'John, can you come here for a minute, please?'

He was out of the bed and beside me in a heartbeat. I silently handed him the stick. He was stunned.

'It has a line. Does that mean yes or no?' I asked him, with a note of urgency in my voice.

'Darling, not only does it mean yes, but there is a little feature on this stick that says three to four weeks. Yes, you are pregnant. In fact, you are three to four weeks pregnant.' We burst into tears of happiness.

We went back to bed and cuddled Oisín, working out the dates and trying to estimate when a new baby might be born. Irish twins, we laughed to each other. There would be just over a year between the babies. Unbelievable.

Then, of course, doubt set in.

Was I really pregnant? It was an old test, possibly as much as two years old. Maybe it had lost some of its power as it lay in my drawer. I started getting nervous, then decided John had to go to the shops for more testing kits and different brands to confirm our suspicions.

I always think shop assistants must laugh when they see a harassed-looking man stocking up on pregnancy tests. I imagine they can picture the scene at home so clearly and the chaos that must be taking place as she waits for him to return with a variety of kits.

I nearly went out of my mind waiting for John to get home from the shop. While he had belted across to Tesco, I had been doing my bit by drinking water for thirty minutes so that I was ready to do my battery of tests.

Yes, test after test confirmed our extraordinary news.

Eventually, I dared to believe in the blue line and we were whooping and hollering around the house, much to our little son's confusion.

It had been such a battle to have our first gorgeous baby yet the second had turned up so quietly and efficiently. It was mind-blowing and we wanted to share our good news. We knew it was ridiculous to tell anybody so early, but after all the bad news and worry recently we wanted to share something good.

John decided that we should go straight away and see my sister Kim to tell her. I rang her and she told me she was with my nieces and nephew in the playground at Rathfarnham Castle. We told her we would join them. She warned us that the weather was dire and that no one else was there, apart from her hardy gang, but we insisted. She probably thought we were crazy but we arrived up to the park and found her hiding in a Wendy house at the side of the playground while her three children were running around in raincoats and wellies, their picnic sandwiches and drinks tucked under their arms. It just seemed the best place in the world to tell her our news.

We ploughed through the muddy playground and she welcomed us to her damp kingdom. We were laughing as we told her we had something to show her and, like two grinning idiots, produced our stick. She shrieked with shock, amazement, joy and excitement, hugged us both tight and started working out dates and time frames. We stood in our little circle, astonished at the wonder of a little white stick with a blue line.

This scene is an extremely important one to me and I replayed it many times over the following dreadful months. Within four days our little world would have collapsed, but I'm so glad that John and I could experience the joy of a surprise pregnancy before the world shifted so shockingly for us. That day, standing in the playground in the rain, nothing seemed as if it could ever go wrong for us. We were so happy, so stunned, and so delirious with the news. It didn't occur to us that our joy could be snatched away.

I spent the next few days hugging myself with delight, thinking frantically about work and trying to establish how I could go back when I would be due to leave again so soon to have another baby. I was in a very strange position because my radio home, *The Gerry Ryan Show*, had disappeared. In the normal scheme of things, I would have sloped back to the office, Gerry would have laughed at me and, probably through gritted teeth, my senior bosses would have waved me off for maternity leave number two.

But now that security blanket was gone. I was going to have a second baby and was going to disappear on maternity leave just months after returning to work. What would happen?

I decided not to panic. John and I were pregnant again, and that was all that mattered. Everything had been so crazy in the aftermath of Gerry's death. Now I tried not to let worry about my future engulf me. John stroked my hair and told me that everything would work out, and I believed him, as he is nearly always right.

On the Wednesday of that week, I suddenly thought that I should ring the hospital and mention the pregnancy to them. I called Clare Glenane, one of the fantastic breast-care nurses in St Vincent's, and asked her to tell Mr Evoy that I was now pregnant in case it affected anything. I was sure it wouldn't but it seemed like the courteous thing to do. Clare congratulated me on our wonderful news and told me that she would, of course, pass it on to him. I hung up and thought no more about it: I was totally consumed with my pregnancy news, and as I had been convinced that my pimple was just a boring old cyst, any niggles I'd had about it simply faded away. I was pregnant and, in my head, nothing else really mattered.

The next day, on Thursday, my dear pal Michael Parke was with us, visiting from London. While we were preparing dinner, John rang to tell us to turn on the radio as he was shortly going live on-air to confirm that, four weeks after Gerry had died, Ryan Tubridy was moving to 2fm to take over Gerry's slot. It was a strange moment. Of course, it was wonderful news that our pal Ryan was going to be working with us but it meant that the *Gerry Ryan Show* era had now finally and completely ended. As we listened to John breaking the news, Michael hugged me close, knowing how tough it was for me to hear its death knell sounded that evening.

Chapter 5

Diagnosis

The next day, Friday, 11 June 2010, just four days after we had discovered our pregnancy, John and I had an appointment with Denis Evoy to get the results of my biopsy and other tests in St Vincent's. Frankly, we were not that worried. John was consumed with his 2fm news and, of course, the pregnancy was the main thing on my mind. I think we were both confident that this thing would turn out to be a cyst. Having done some research on the web, I was reassured that my pimple could not be confused with a lump, which was the conventional presentation of breast cancers, so I was quite calm as we sat in the waiting room.

Our appointment was for two thirty and John's parents

were minding Oisín for the afternoon. I had talked to his mum, Margaret, about the medical investigations but had made light of it, assuring her that it was just something that would have to be removed at some stage. After working seven days a week for the past six weeks, John had taken the afternoon off and we had made a plan to get the results, discuss the procedure that would have to happen and head off to Dún Laoghaire to grab a bite to eat and walk along the pier before heading back to pick up the baby.

At this stage, only John's parents and Kim knew what was going on. We hadn't told anyone else – after all, what was there to tell them? No one cares about a cyst.

As we sat in the waiting room, my memory is of sweltering heat – in fact, all of my memories of that summer are of heat and brilliant sunshine. People came and went, some to be ushered in ahead of us, but I was still unconcerned. I had had health skirmishes before but luckily nothing too serious. Clare Glenane eventually came down and called us in to meet Denis. We stood up and followed her down the hall, chatting politely about the gorgeous weather.

I remember it being a small white room with a hospital-type gurney in the corner. Two chairs were backed against the window for us and there was a desk where Denis was sitting and another chair behind him for Clare. As we walked in Denis greeted us and asked me to undress so that he could examine my breast again.

I stepped behind the curtain and started taking the layers off. A novice in this world, I hadn't expected an examination so had dressed badly for it. I'm now an expert and I know you wear one layer, preferably with buttons for quick access. That day I was an amateur and was wearing a complicated t-shirt top and a vest over my bra. I undressed as quickly as I could. Then Denis had a quick look and returned to his desk, leaving me to put my tops back on. I noticed that the atmosphere in the room had subtly changed: something was different. I distinctly remember starting to shake a little bit and I couldn't get the damn clothes back on quickly enough. It seemed to take me for ever to finish dressing and I was cursing myself for having picked such a stupid outfit. The room was eerily quiet. There was no chat between John and the others and, as Denis was obviously not going to say anything until I was back on my chair, I was beginning to panic as I tried to snap my bra quickly into place. Eventually I was ready. Of course, in reality it probably took about thirty seconds but it felt like forever.

I returned to my seat, looked at Denis and said, 'Well?'

He looked me straight in the eye and said, quietly but clearly, 'Evelyn, I'm terribly sorry to tell you this but there were anomalies in your results. I'm afraid there is a problem.'

I just stared at him.

The silence in the room took on a life of its own. It grew and it swelled and it threatened to drown me but I couldn't think of any way to stop it. My mind was filling with the sound of crashing waves. Anomalies. What did that mean? Jesus Christ, he was telling me it was cancer.

Christ, I had cancer. I was going to die.

I remember suddenly clearly thinking, I need to find out what the story is right now. I cleared my throat and placed my trembling hands on my lap. 'Denis, are you telling me that I have cancer?'

'Yes,' he replied.

And then I asked him the question that I still cannot believe I had the strength and courage to ask. I looked him straight in the eye and said, 'I have a six-month-old baby at home and I am now pregnant so I need this answer. Is it terminal?'

And with that John collapsed in the seat beside me.

It turns out that he had become suspicious that something was wrong back in the waiting area. He had noticed that lots of other patients were coming and going, having had their consultations, and we were being left to the end. He had figured that that was not good.

He had walked into that room with a bad feeling and his anxiety had begun to build then. Later he said that after Denis had examined me he had returned to his desk and started scribbling, without looking at him. That was when he became convinced that bad news was coming. By the time Denis gave us the diagnosis, John was in a state of total panic and my uncharacteristically blunt question was the final straw. He simply passed out.

As he slumped beside me, everything in the room started to get swimmy, and when I turned to him, his head was thrown back, his face a horrible greeny-white, and he had beads of cold sweat on his forehead. Seeing him like that, I felt a wave of nausea. Then I thought, He's going to die now. I remember looking at the floor and, for one second, it seemed to crack and break up. I thought I was going to fall through into the centre of the earth. Then I told myself sharply, *No* – you've been through something like this crap before and you survived. Breathe. Breathe. Breathe. You know this moment. This moment when your world explodes around you because of a few simple words. Back in 1998, when they rang to tell you that Daddy had died suddenly, your world shattered into pieces but you survived it. You know this cruel moment and it passes. So breathe. Breathe.

Then I remember saying to myself, Evelyn, you need to stay really calm now, calm, calm, calm. This has all gone crazy and you need to stay calm.

By this stage Clare had leapt up, and she and Denis were with John. I took his hand as he came around and whispered into his ear, 'John, John, I need you. The babies and I need you. You need to come back now and take care of us. You need to come around and sit up and mind us now. We can't do this now.'

Clare led John over to the gurney and he lay down, apologising for causing a fuss. His collapse broke the ice: I teased him that I was the one who'd got the news, not him, so I should be the one stretched out on the bed. I told him later that it was actually the most romantic thing he had ever done for me as it proved he really loved me.

But back to that question. Back to me asking the most horrific question anyone ever has to utter in a doctor's room: 'Is it terminal? I need to know.'

In fairness, Denis himself seemed about to collapse with shock. '*Whaat?* No, no, absolutely not.'

And with that he had given me a precious weapon. Because in the dark, horrible days and weeks ahead, when I was convulsed with fear that it was going to return and take everything away from me, John would stroke my bald head and say, over and over again, 'Remember back to that day with Denis. Remember his face? Remember how shocked he was that you were even thinking that? If he had had to tell you the news that day, he would have. He didn't. He was shocked by your question too.'

Poor John would say these and a few other things that became mantras to get me through the darkness ahead as I lay on our bed sobbing with fear that I was going to die. 'Remember back to that day with Denis. Remember his face? Remember how shocked he was that you were even thinking that?' Over and over and over again. Which brings me to a side point about the vital importance of how you tell people devastating news.

My dad, Pascal, had died unexpectedly of a heart attack in 1998 when I was twenty-five. He was just sixty-one. He was the fittest, sportiest man I knew and I adored him.

I was working and living in Galway at the time, and when they rang from home with the terrible news, Celine Curtin, a fantastic friend of mine, was the one to break it to me and she dealt with me so gently and kindly that her words really offered me comfort in the torturous months ahead. The way Denis and Clare had dealt so sympathetically and professionally with us really helped in the months ahead too, and I am now firmly convinced that the way you tell people devastating news is vitally important.

The words, the phrases, the mood of the room, the expressions on the faces of those dealing with you in a moment of crisis really matter as you mull over and try to absorb the effects of devastating news for years to come. You relive those moments, examining them, desperate to make sense of it all, so everything that happens at that particular time becomes exaggerated. If you have been told something clearly yet sympathetically, it can help you deal with it, no matter how terrible the situation. In the months after the diagnosis I was so thankful that it was Clare and Denis who had told me my horrible news, not some faceless doctor in a busy hallway.

But back to that room and the reality that I had just received my third piece of life-changing news in a few short weeks. First Gerry, then the pregnancy and now this. As John lay there, mortified, Denis turned to me and – I remember this so clearly – he asked, 'Evelyn, when did the pregnancy happen?'

I started apologising to him. which was obviously

ridiculous, but it was such a tense, frightening meeting that all normal rules had flown out the window. 'I'm so sorry,' I said. 'Just on Monday, we only found out on Monday.'

He went on to explain to me that they had all been stunned to discover the biopsy results. The multidisciplinary team had gone through all the cases that morning, and subsequently a colleague of his told me that there had been total shock in the room when my biopsy was confirmed as having cancer cells. As I had rung Clare during the week to tell her about the pregnancy, I presume that at that Friday-morning meeting many of them would have heard that twist in the tale for the first time, hence the added shockwaves.

In fairness to Denis, from his perspective this was now getting tricky. I had landed into his waiting room two weeks before with a fairly straightforward-looking thing on my breast and now it had turned out to be cancerous and I had gone from being a normal patient to a pregnant one – a first-trimester pregnant one at that.

Things moved quickly. Now we knew that there was some sort of tumour, Denis explained to me that I would be whisked off to have a mammogram to get a clearer picture of my breast. So far, we had been relying on the biopsy and now they needed more information to work out what would happen next, hence the mammogram. He asked if I was OK to get it done there and then, and I said, yes, of course.

Within minutes, it seemed, of my hearing the diagnosis,

Denis and I were on our way down to the mammogram room. On the walk, I felt oddly clear-headed. I hadn't cried a tear. One part of my brain was whirring away, repeating, 'Cancer, cancer, cancer,' but my main thought was that, now I had Denis to myself, I needed to ask questions and start working out the situation for myself.

So I started with an easy one. I asked him why I had got the cancer. He then gave me some advice that has stuck with me and helped me through many dark moments. He told me that they didn't know. That they would never know why I'd got it. He added that I should stop focusing on that and focus now on the treatment, recovery and on getting my life back on track. So, I'd learnt that another evil aspect of cancer is that often they don't know why you get it. They can speculate, advise, deduce, factor in this, that and the other but, fundamentally, the key to accepting many cancers, in my view, is that you have to understand that, once you've taken responsible steps to achieving good health – you're not smoking, drinking too much, eating crappy food – it can often just be a case of dumb luck.

People get cancer all the time, people get all sorts of cancers every day, and, really, there's often no reason why one seemingly healthy person gets it over another and for many of us, sadly, it just comes down to chance.

When we got to the mammogram room, Denis handed me over to the care of a nurse and there and then I had my first mammogram.

The mammogram is an amazingly simple test that had terrified me for years and now I had to have one under the most stressful of circumstances. I did not have time to panic and, of course, there is nothing to be scared of about the test itself. The nurse gently explained to me that I would have to remove the top half of my clothes. When I was ready, she would walk me over to the machine, and each breast would be scanned separately. I would rest one breast on a kind of metal shelf and then she would press down on it and create a clamp to take a picture of the breast. She would repeat the exercise with the other. It wouldn't take long, she promised.

All I really remember is that it was cold, and that the nurse went on to tell me kindly that her mum had been diagnosed years ago with breast cancer but was in great shape now. A few minutes later, mammogram over, I left the room and realised I still hadn't shed a tear, which was weird as I'm the kind of person who cries over the most ridiculous and cheesy television ads. I would have expected in those circumstances to have dribbled away down the plughole by now, but no. I suppose I was just numbed by the nightmare. I had no roadmap for dealing with a cancer diagnosis so I had no clue how to react. Instead of sobbing, I felt strangely calm and in control. From the minute I had heard the terrible news, I had started forming questions and I just knew I needed answers. That was now my focus. Tears could wait. I needed rock-solid information now. I had had cancer for about forty minutes and already I was on a mission to get at the root of this shocking news.

I thanked the nurse ever so politely, and I quickly left the mammogram room and returned to the examining room where John and Clare were waiting for me. As I walked in, they were chatting and turned to me. Clare ushered me towards a chair. I had just sat down when the door opened and Dr Ann O'Doherty burst into the room.

She had performed my biopsy and had been one of the team who had been so shocked by my result that morning. She was to prove an incredible ally to myself and John over the coming weeks. We all started talking urgently, with Ann telling us that now I was pregnant we had serious thinking and planning to do. She and Clare started going through the process. Because of the pregnancy, they couldn't send me for an MRI scan as it would be harmful to the baby: we should take the weekend to discuss the implications of that and return on Tuesday to begin discussions around treatment options.

Ann then gently but clearly said to us, 'Now, Evelyn and John, I want to say this to you. Take one step at a time, otherwise it can be too overwhelming. Take your time. No rush. We have plenty of time to work this all out. Don't make *any* decisions before you have to.' She was very clear on that point and keen to make sure we had heard what she'd said. We nodded mutely at her, our minds swirling. Then she went on to say that the next step was to discuss treatment options with Denis.

'Treatment options,' I repeated. 'Oh, yes. We'd need to discuss them.' I nodded confidently although I hadn't the first clue what she meant.

Then Denis returned and the three of them were very calm and confident that we could work this out. 'Oh, yes,' I agreed again. 'Of course, we can work this out. This is all very workable outable.' I nodded enthusiastically but all I could feel was a drowning sense of disbelief.

The memory of that conversation is deeply upsetting and still leaves me breathless. I had entered that building as one of them, a 'civilian', and now I was firmly in the 'patient' camp. They were so supportive and friendly that I felt like one of the team for a minute but then I remembered that the only reason I was standing there, the focus of their attention, was because suddenly, out of nowhere, I now had breast cancer. I was saying all the right things, murmuring in agreement as we discussed scans and time frames, but it was the most surreal experience.

While I was nodding outwardly, inwardly my mind was exploding. I had been told I had cancer, out of the blue, just an hour ago, and suddenly I was in that huddle, calmly discussing options and timing. It was horrendous. Within a frighteningly short period of time, I had crossed a line into a new world. And none of those lovely people, helpful and all as they were, was there with me. I was on my own. My baby and I were now in this new world and while I may have carried off a performance of a mature, responsible patient that day, inside I felt like I would never again take a sweet, calm breath of air into my lungs. At one stage Ann took my hand and said to me, 'I know that this is the blackest day of your life. You are reeling with shock and you cannot imagine life ever being happy again but I promise you that this will pass.'

Those kind words stuck with me for months afterwards and really helped me through some of the more painful days ahead.

They sent us off home to just absorb the news, and they made a return appointment for Tuesday at midday and we quietly left the room, holding hands, to make our way down the corridor. I kept thinking of Ann's kind words. She had advised us to go home, let the news sink in over the weekend and we would have more discussions the following week. Now her meaning began to sink in. No rush. No need for drama. No urgency. This sounded like excellent advice to me and I took it to heart.

As a woman you live in fear of cancer, particularly breast cancer. You associate it with misery, hair loss, pain and scars and death. Yes, you know the women who survive it are amazing and you are filled with admiration for them, but you never, ever want to be one of them, thanks very much. Now I was going to be 'one of those women' and I still didn't know what the worst part might be. Would I lose my breast? Probably. My hair, definitely. My mind, possibly. I had walked into St Vincent's Hospital less than two hours ago a normal (if slightly pregnant) woman and there I was, two hours later, pregnant with breast cancer.

Jesus, I'd really done it this time.

Chapter 6

Breaking the News

You may think that the world changes the minute you walk out of a doctor's room with a cancer diagnosis, but of course it doesn't.

As I left the hospital, shell-shocked, I suddenly realised that John wasn't beside me. I stopped and looked back – he was at the car-park pay machine, rummaging through his jeans pockets for change. I looked at all the people lined up behind him, waiting impatiently, and thought, they just do not know. They have no idea what has just happened to us. Maybe I should tell them. Maybe I should hop up on a chair, clap my hands to get their attention and say, 'Excuse me, ladies and gentlemen, but my husband and I have just been told some rather "interesting" news, which has pushed the whole paying-for-parking job down our list a bit, so bear with us.' Standing there, it was just bizarre to think that if we failed to dig out eight euro in the next two seconds we'd probably be lynched. It struck me that hospitals should have a policy where they discreetly slip you a voucher for your parking after they've given you a positive cancer diagnosis. It would be very helpful.

We paid the damn parking and headed towards the car. Once inside, we fell back into our seats.

'What now?' John asked.

'Kim. We have to tell Kim now.'

My heart was hammering as I turned on my phone to call her. I rang her and there was no answer. It was only later that I discovered she had been ringing our phones all afternoon. When they had both remained switched off, she had felt a rising sense of panic, hopped into her car and was now rushing frantically around St Vincent's trying to find us.

I tried her again and this time she answered. I said I was on my way to her house, which was just a few minutes away, and that we would meet her there. She got in just before us. When she opened the door she looked at me and just knew. John went out into the garden to distract our nieces and nephew, while Kim and I sat calmly in the sitting room. I blurted out the facts; she nodded and asked all the right questions. Then I told her I was dreading telling our mother Peigí and asked her to do the cruellest thing: I asked her to tell Mum for me. She immediately said, yes, she would talk to her that evening.

John and I had to go then because I was desperate to pick up the baby from his grandparents'. We hugged, and then headed off to Templeogue to collect Oisín. We knocked at the door and were welcomed in, where Ois was happily playing with his toys. I picked him up and hugged him tightly as John asked his parents to sit down.

'We have good news and bad news. The good news is that, although it's very early days, Evelyn is pregnant. The bad news is that the diagnosis has been confirmed and she has breast cancer.'

Margaret cried, Brian looked absolutely shocked and John was still pale. All I could think was, What have I done to these people? These lovely wonderful people did not deserve this misery. I know how ridiculous it sounds but you feel extremely guilty when you get a diagnosis like that. You think you're responsible for it in some way, and that you're wrecking other people's lives with your news. I whispered, 'I'm so sorry,' into Oisín's ear and it was something I would repeat over and over endlessly, torturing myself in the months ahead. I used to lie beside his cot at night, crying over him, saying, 'I'm so sorry, I'm so sorry' over and over again.

Until the diagnosis, I used to put the baby to sleep by telling him, 'Go to sleep, baby, and Mama will see you in the morning.' Now that confidence had been shattered. How could I say it any more when I had no clue what lay ahead the following day? My little mantra had been infected with the diagnosis.

That first afternoon, I slowly began to learn how this kind of news can rot a family. As we spoke to our parents and siblings, I saw how cancer darkens every light thing. Telling my family I had cancer was like getting a bucket of black, slimy oil, dipping them into it and watching them try desperately to clean it off.

Getting a cancer diagnosis is without doubt the most violent thing that has ever happened to me. It smacked me, it punched me, it clawed at me, it bit me, it chewed me, it savaged me.

But, somehow, it did not destroy me. It nearly did. It threatened to many times but somehow I got through it and now, writing this three years later, parts of it are already a blur. Sitting here now, I realise that this is why I am writing it all down because if you are given a cancer diagnosis but the prognosis is OK, it can actually pass. You can get your life back. But that was unthinkable on that horrific June Friday.

So, what do I remember of the first evening after I'd received my shocking diagnosis? Well, I remember going home with John and the baby and I still hadn't cried. I have the clearest memory of standing at our kitchen table and resting my hand gently on it and thinking, I don't know how to do this. I have no super powers. I'm just an ordinary thirty-eight-year-old woman who has a six-month-old baby and another on the way. Not so unusual, and now this. And I said to myself again and again, I do not know how to do this.

I said it out loud to John as he was getting Oisín ready for bed around eight o'clock and he sensibly replied that no one knew straight after a diagnosis how to handle this situation, so we were going to have to take it minute by minute. Minute by torturous minute. But how would that work?

Then I realised that John was producing us.

He had been producing live programmes for a very long time and he was bringing the order you need in a busy live studio to the chaos we had suddenly been thrown into at home. All that matters for a presenter during a live show can be summed up as 'now and next' and that was what we were going to do. We were going to focus on getting the baby changed, his bottle ready and putting him to bed. Next we would deal with planning our dinner. Nothing more than that. We would focus on the next five minutes and the next and so on, until we had put in the day. And it worked: with that one exchange we had stumbled on our survival strategy for the next year. Now and next. We were going to break down life into little five- and ten-minute blocks, parsing time until the nightmare ended.

By now it was around half past eight and there was a long, dark evening ahead of us as we trudged our way downstairs from the baby's room to the kitchen. Within minutes, my mum was at the door. I had asked Kim to tell her the news and I knew, from the way the bell was furiously ringing, that she had done so. I don't know why I couldn't face telling her myself but I think I knew it was going to be too painful. Mum had handled my dad's death with such dignity all those years ago that maybe I felt I was going to break her still-healing heart again and I couldn't bear the responsibility for doing that. All I know is that I'm glad Kim agreed to tell her for me and of course, once Kim had told her she had come running to our door.

John opened the door to her and she came straight in. She found me in the kitchen and threw her arms around me. We stood there clinging to each other for dear life. It actually felt like that. We had been there, in that very kitchen, when my darling dad had died in 1998 and it was dreadful to think that I was the cause of even more pain for her. After a few minutes, we sat down at the table and went over the events of the day.

We drank a lot of tea. I had drunk decaf tea during my first pregnancy but that night I told John that I'd only be able to get through with regular tea so Barry's tea went into the pot. The poor man. It was only later I realised that if I'd told him I'd be jumping to the moon, he would have said, 'Very wise,' and supported me all the way.

So, how did we fill that first evening? Unbelievably, I struggle now to remember. The hours after that kind of diagnosis are very strange. You feel so vulnerable and fragile and you keep thinking about other people and how they must have reacted over the years. I was so confused that night because I found it difficult to accept that on the one hand my body was functioning perfectly, full throttle with the pregnancy, and on the other, just inches away from my womb, it was generating cancerous cells.

How could I be creating life and destroying it at the same time?

Eventually, Mum got up to leave and offered to take Oisín with her for a sleepover so we could rest in the morning, but he was so cosy in his cot that we decided to leave him there. We said our goodnights and then we finally peeled ourselves away from the kettle and the kitchen table and staggered, exhausted, up to bed.

Incredibly, I slept. For a while.

At about three a.m. I woke with a start because I thought there was a creature in the room. Through my half-closed eyes, I was sure I saw a dark tail disappearing around the bedroom door, then heard padding down the stairs. I was so frightened. I clambered out of bed, looked out into the garden and there it was. A horrible black scary wolf. A cliché wolf straight from every stupid horror movie you've ever seen. Ridiculous, I know.

That was the first night the wolf appeared to me and I was to see him regularly over the next few months, just spotting him out of the corner of my eye. He was regularly there at night, circling my home and my beautiful family. It was terrifying.

I slowly turned from the window and got back into

bed. Eventually I fell asleep again but I was haunted by a series of strange and upsetting dreams. At one stage, I was in a cave and couldn't see my way out when I suddenly glimpsed some light falling from a lamp. I felt my way along the cave wall and made out the face of my brother Brian as he held up a lamp. The cave grew brighter and brighter as I saw the faces of each of my family, and there they were, like some holiday snap, Kim, my brothers Brian and Colm, all surrounded by my brothers and sisters in law. I could just make out Kim's husband, Norman, Brian's wife, Maria, and Colm's wife Anita in the half light, as well as John's brothers and their wives, Evin and Claire, Brian and Sue, all of them holding old-style gas lamps.

I woke up to feel my face damp with tears. As I lay quietly in the dark, I realised that John was awake too. We curled up together and he suggested that we needed to get Oisín and bring him into the bed with us. He went into the baby's room, carried him in from the cot and laid him between us. He hardly stirred. No parenting manual would agree with what we did but we needed him right beside us that night and the next and the next. For the following months, the baby was regularly in our bed, lying between the two of us, delighted with himself. The comfort his little sleepy presence gave us was immeasurable. During that horrendous time we needed him far more than he needed us.

Getting out of bed the next morning, I felt like I had

been run down by a truck. The news of the diagnosis and the pregnancy were fighting for attention in my brain, like two small children scrapping over a favourite toy. Then the ticker-tape started. The scrolling on-screen news banner, like the one on rolling-news stations, began that morning and continued for months. The words 'I AM PREGNANT' and 'I HAVE BREAST CANCER' were written on the banner. These stupid words, 'I have breast cancer and I am pregnant', just rolled around and around and around my brain for months. Even as I was idly chatting to someone the ticker-tape never stopped. It was exhausting.

Somehow we crawled through the weekend and filled the time by doing things like walking to my sister's house rather than taking the car. All the time, the ticker-tape was scrolling around my poor scrambled brain. We walked miles that weekend, pushing Oisín along in his buggy. We spent much of the time talking about our news, of course, but not all of it. We would have short, intense bursts of conversation about the diagnosis, then, unbelievably, we would get back to talking about normal things, like what we would have for dinner that evening.

It was very odd. One minute, I would be talking about the traffic or something inane, and the next John would blurt out something profound about our diagnosis and we would have a passionate discussion for a while about whatever point he had raised and then just as quickly fall into silence as our exhausted brains tried to keep up with all that had happened.

Every so often, one of us would say, 'But in the middle of all this, there is a baby on the way,' and we would stop, hug each other and smile in delight at Oisín. Then we would be quiet again as both of us tried to work out how a cancer diagnosis affected a pregnancy. Over the years, I had had some experience of breast cancer with friends of mine so I had an idea that the treatment usually involved surgery and chemotherapy. From the little I knew, it was clear that chemotherapy was a horribly toxic regime so John and I began discussing what other options might be available to our doctors: there was clearly no question of a pregnant patient getting chemotherapy.

We were so excited about this new baby, so the more we thought about it, it seemed to me that there was only one solution. I decided, in my infinite wisdom, that once the baby had been safely delivered, I would begin my treatment. It seemed to be the only option that made sense, so I started mentally preparing myself for that course of action. I know how naïve it sounds and possibly a bit stupid, but at that point, I didn't understand the demands of the world of cancer. I wanted the baby so much that I prioritised it over everything else. I figured that we could do a bit of surgery, remove the tumour, and delay chemo until after the baby was born. Really, what did a couple of months matter in the overall scheme? I shake my head now when I think of the mad conclusion I reached all by myself in my own head. What was I thinking?

I had no idea of the vice-like grip that a diagnosis takes on your life. I thought *I* could control it, and that if I chose my baby over treatment, everything could still be fine. I had no real sense of how serious the situation was and that cancer could spread so fast that it had to be tackled aggressively. I was gloriously naïve about it all. Then again, maybe naïvety got me through that horrific weekend. Going to bed on Sunday night, I told myself it would all be grand. I would have my surgery, then the baby, then chemo and radiotherapy. Grand so, I concluded. Solution found.

Writing this, I still have no idea how we got through that weekend, but I suppose chopping it up into five-minute sections must have helped. The diagnosis was a shadow that stalked us the whole time, and by Sunday night the only comfort we had was that we would never have to go through that weekend again. We had avoided everyone except our family as we couldn't trust ourselves to carry on a normal conversation with anyone else. Already, our diagnosis was dramatically changing our lives. (By the way, my husband likes to point out that whenever our wedding is mentioned it is 'my wedding', but when it comes to the diagnosis it is 'our diagnosis' and 'our treatment'!)

John somehow got through work on Monday and I spent the day with Mum and Kim, drinking more tea and talking, talking, talking.

Eventually, after all the chats and the discussions, Tuesday came and our follow-up consultation appointment with Denis Evoy where we would discuss the options available to us. We had no idea what lay ahead. We knew the two facts, that we were dealing with cancer and a pregnancy, but we had absolutely no handle on how they would be treated and, more importantly, how they would impact on each other. We went to a bagel shop on our way into the hospital, which set a pattern for that entire summer: we lived on bagels, takeaways or lasagnes left on our doorsteps by friends and family.

As we arrived into Reception on that beautifully sunny day, I was beginning to feel like I was living a secret life. At this stage the only people who knew our news were our medical team, of course, John's parents, and my mother and sister. We had decided not to tell anyone else until we had more definite information.

Grainne Griffin, our breast-care nurse that day, guided us into the 'nice' patients' lounge, with couches, flowers and water. This was clearly the setting where bad news was discussed and I panicked. I had hardly sat down when I had to jump up and pace the room, apologising to Grainne but explaining that I had to keep moving.

A few minutes later, when Denis came in to discuss our diagnosis I was still marching around the room. By this time I was feeling very strange and unsure of myself. I was shaking badly. Everything we had discussed during the past fragile weekend was now, suddenly, a horrible reality. We had spent time mulling over the language associated with cancer, but we had been talking about the terms used as if they were a slightly familiar foreign language. Now, parading around that room, I realised the terminology related to me and that I had no distance from a medical nightmare. I had breast cancer. I had a *tumour*. This sterile punch of a word was now in my world and it was going to have endless consequences for John and myself. I shook some more and looked at the crumpled piece of paper in my hand. It was full of questions.

At moments of clarity during the weekend, we had started writing them down in case we forgot to mention them to Denis and some crucial detail would be lost. We had many issues to put to the team that day and the first of them was, of course, the baby. What did this news mean for the baby? As I scanned the list in my hand, I was practically jogging around the place at this point.

I quickly explained to Denis that I was not capable of sitting down for our meeting, so I was going to walk around the room, if that was OK. I was quite agitated and I presume he and Grainne threw each other a few looks when he gloriously suggested that we could take the appointment outside into the gardens, if I preferred. I nearly wept with relief. Perfect. And so this little bunch of people slowly made their way out into the sunshine, Grainne on the left, Denis next, then me and then John. We walked and talked for an hour and I will be forever grateful to Denis for offering me that option. Heading out to the gardens with Denis and Grainne, I instantly felt calmer and my thoughts stopped jumbling crazily. On our way, he reiterated again the message that Ann had given me that we were in no rush and had plenty of time to discuss everything about this unique situation.

Once we had established our route around the flowerbeds, the serious talk began. Denis told us he had been thinking about our situation over the weekend and, because the pregnancy was at such an early point, he wanted to be extremely careful about the treatment options. Usually, he said, they would send a patient with positive biopsy results off for more scans but he was ruling out MRI or any such radiology options as the risks would be profound for the baby. This left him with a problem, though: while the biopsy had confirmed the presence of cancerous cells in my right breast, without scans he could not accurately assess the actual size of the tumour. He was going to have to perform a lumpectomy, with me under a general anaesthetic. Before we had a chance to cross-examine him about the differences between a lumpectomy and a mastectomy, he asked us how we felt about the pregnancy. We described how excited we had been when we'd discovered it just the week before. We admitted that we were now confused and distraught at the consequences of the diagnosis, and now that we had the baby to think of we had no real understanding of how the situation could be managed. I mentioned that over the weekend I had reconciled myself to having the baby, and then starting whatever treatment would be recommended. While I rambled on about the joys of pregnancy, John wanted assurances about my health and treatment. It was an extremely intense meeting with the four of us walking along, heads bowed, deep in conversation.

Denis and Grainne were so discreet, so beautifully subtle in what they said to us, that the phrase 'breast cancer' had not really been used. Eventually I blurted out, 'I have a stupid question – do I actually have breast cancer as such?'

'Yes,' Denis replied.

'Fine. That clarifies things,' I responded.

It quickly became clear that the treatment Denis had in mind for me had three strands, surgery, chemotherapy and radiotherapy, and they would begin immediately. The surgery should just involve a lumpectomy (a central core excision), which meant that I would lose a partial amount of my breast but it is not as invasive as a mastectomy, where the full breast is removed. They would then move on to chemotherapy and finish with a course of radiotherapy. The surgery would (hopefully) remove the tumour, the chemotherapy would kill off any lingering cancer cells and the radiotherapy would prevent any such cells left in the body from growing. This, he assured us, should all be done and dusted within a year

Right. A year. But how did that work? Now, I was really confused. I was only a few weeks pregnant and we still had many months to go before the baby would be born. How could the treatment be over within twelve months?

'Denis,' I said, 'I don't understand. I'm only a few weeks pregnant, the baby has another seven or eight months to go, so all these things you're saying, surgery and chemo and radiotherapy, how does that work with the baby? I want to have this baby.'

He paused and smiled gently at me. 'Evelyn, you can have the baby but you need to have your treatment. You're only thirty-eight, so with someone as young as you, we need to start treatment immediately.

I began to stutter, 'But, Denis, if I have the baby – you – how does – I mean – preg— and surgeries – and chemo … I don't underst— What are you saying?'

Then the bombshell. 'Evelyn, you can have surgery and chemotherapy quite safely during pregnancy.'

Whaaaat? You can WHAT?

Boom! Another explosion in my head. I liked and trusted Denis, but now I was totally confused. I couldn't quite understand the words he was sharing with me. 'Please,' I begged. 'Please explain like I'm a child. Just keep it really stupidly simple. How does this work because it sounds crazy to me. Chemo in pregnancy sounds impossible.'

He took his time to confirm that it was possible to administer chemotherapy safely during pregnancy.

This was the first time I had ever heard that. Chemotherapy during pregnancy? How was it possible? How did they even know that it would work?

This made no sense to me. Everything I knew about chemotherapy was horrible. You lose your hair, you are constantly nauseous and you are told that it rips you apart: how could you possibly hope for a healthy pregnancy during chemotherapy? It went against every notion I had ever held dear about pregnancy. Growing a baby means lots of rest, nutritious food, exercise, no caffeine, no alcohol, nothing to excess. How could this man seriously be suggesting we could ditch all that learnt wisdom and, instead of taking vitamins, start pumping poisons into my body? You weren't even supposed to eat bloody prawns during pregnancy, for Christ's sake, so how could chemotherapy drugs not obliterate this tiny fragment of a person?

If my mind had been swirling before, now it had collapsed into a sodden marsh. I felt old and tired and swamped by all this new detail, and the terrible decisions we were facing. Eventually Denis said we all needed more information on my condition so, in the absence of scans, the best thing to do was for him to book me in for surgery so that he could take a look and assess the situation. That was also the first time I had heard of lymph nodes. He told me that while he would be performing a lumpectomy to remove the tumour, he would also be taking a lymph node sample from under my arm.

I nodded knowledgeably. Ah yes, a lumpectomy, and lymph-node assessment. Last week, I'd had only a passing relationship with these words but now I was facing into having them dominate my world and I still barely knew what they meant.

'Tell me again,' I begged. 'Denis, start from the beginning. I go in one morning and what happens?'

'You come into me early that morning. We give you an anaesthetic and perform a lumpectomy. That means we will remove "the pimple", as you call it, and all the tissue around and behind it. The procedure is called a "central sector excision".'

'So it's like boring through an apple. You're basically drilling into the middle of the core,' I interrupted.

'Eh, well, yes, kind of,' Denis answered, a little stunned by my bluntness, I think.

'OK, now I get it,' I said. 'First you remove the pimple, which we know from the biopsy is cancerous. You're not removing the whole breast, just the area we know about from the biopsy. But what are you doing with my lymph nodes?'

Denis explained what would happen then, which seemed to boil down to this. Groups of lymph nodes are located in the neck, underarms, chest, abdomen and groin, and they are important parts of the body's immune system. Many types of cancer spread through the lymphatic system: if mine had spread, it would have gone into the lymph nodes near the tumour site on my right breast.

To test the area, Denis was going to have to find a

lymph node or gland called the 'sentinel lymph node', the first lymph node to which cancer cells are most likely to spread from a primary tumour. You have lots and lots of lymph nodes in your body – and in your armpit area it ranges from twenty to forty – but the medical team need to find the key one, the sentinel, to work out what is really happening and for this they use a radioactive dye. On the morning of the surgery, they would inject the dye into my right breast to show up the sentinel node by travelling to my armpit. Using the dye, the surgeons would locate the sentinel node, remove it and test it to see if it carried any markers for cancer. This information is important in determining the progression of your cancer and individualising cancer treatment for maximum benefit. If the cancer had spread it would be found in the sentinel node, and if the sample was positive, there was a chance that I would have a second operation to clear the remaining lymph nodes. Removing the lymph nodes would prevent the cancer spreading around the rest of my body.

At this stage we did not know how extensive the cancer was, so we all agreed that surgery was necessary and soon.

Fine. Book me in so.

Are you free Thursday?

Sure, Thursday is good. I have nothing on. Oh, except for my life. Except for all the outings and playdates organised for my gorgeous baby boy and the visits to friends and family carefully tapped into my phone. The speed at which all this was happening was terrifying. Just last Friday morning I had been on the phone organising my book-club summer dinner for this Thursday night: now one look at John's face confirmed to me that I would be missing the book-club summer dinner this year. That was only the start of it. It was June, and we were supposed to have many summer months ahead of us for fun with Oisín and planning our second baby's entrance into the world. Suddenly and so cruelly it had all been decimated. It turns out that after all the excitement and joy around the news of our second baby, now my life was confusing and strange. I did not know what was happening to me anymore. Standing there among the heartbreakingly beautiful flowerbeds we said goodbye to my old life.

As I looked around, nothing seemed solid. I had known I was pregnant with our second baby for just over a week and now all the elation had evaporated. Out of nowhere, I was launched into a new, unknown, frightening world full of phrases and terms I didn't understand – but while I might not have been familiar with the medical expressions, I knew the emotions I would be experiencing. Fear, worry, anger, loneliness. I knew it was all in train for me now but Denis had made it clear that I had no choice. The treatment could not be delayed. I had to get started if I wanted to live.

And, boy, did I want to live.

I wanted to live and live and live and live and live and

live and live. So, instead of heading into a lovely restaurant next Thursday, I was now headed to an operating theatre and, from what Denis was saying, that was only the beginning. So, Thursday it was. Book us in.

I want to live.

Dear Ross,
Hello.

I should introduce myself to you. I am your mother and we probably need to sort out a couple of things now.

First, regardless of anything else that is happening, we are so delighted that you are on your way.

Second, although it seems we have a bit to go until you make it home to us safely, it will be fine. I'm sure of it. I am your mother, and mothers are always right.

To me there is just one important thing in the middle of all this madness. You have turned up and we are so pleased that Daddy's and my heart could burst with happiness. You are so welcome, a chroí. On the June day when we found out that you are on your way, we screamed with delight; life was wonderful again. And, yes, within a few short days we were plunged into a nightmare with the diagnosis, but I need you to know that having this trace of you inside me is helping to keep me sane and happy in this darkest of times. Why?

Well, you have a brother. He is Oisín and he is the most gorgeous, funny, bright, smart baby anyone could want.

Whenever I think of him, I know that every step we have to take on this road to get you home safely to us will be worth it because of him. If you are in any way like the baby he is, then any trauma will be worth it because he is so amazing. He constantly thrills me and I am continually stunned by the love Daddy and I feel for him.

And, just like with you, our love for him sparked from the minute we discovered that he was on his way to us. From the confirmation that I was pregnant we talked about him all the time, and made plans and promises to each other about the love we would show him. He was my constant companion for nine months, and all the time when I was pregnant with him, I'd rest my hand on my bump and wonder about the person inside me. Who would this baby turn out to be? What kind of child would he grow into?

In fact, we waited so long for him to come along that, at times, I wondered if any baby could live up to our expectations, but as soon as our wonder baby was handed to us, our world burst into colour. He was so perfect that, on the first day in hospital, I asked myself if we were good enough for him. Seeing him grow and change since those early days after his birth has been an unending joy and that is why I am vaguely calm this nightmarish weekend.

He has brought us such joy, such contentment, such fun (such nappies!), that I would walk through fire for him. Now it seems that I may be asked to do just that for you, but I am sure it is going to be fine. Because of him, even the promise of you is enough to keep my feet solidly plodding along, stumbling at times, but generally plodding along. Another version of Oisín in our lives? Yes, please. Anything. Anywhere. Anytime. Two babies in our home? Oh, please, yes.

Rossy, you will be my new constant companion for the next few months. You can help guide me through this nightmare and, I promise, we will meet and it will be wonderful and we will all live. All of us. We will live and live and live and be happy.

No rush. We'll take our time,

Oceans of love,

Mama

Chapter 7

Decisions

We left St Vincent's on the Tuesday afternoon, reeling. Neither of us had ever heard of chemotherapy being done during pregnancy and we knew that we would have to do some research into it. But, as I kept reminding John, we had to be careful not to get too carried away. Until the surgery on Thursday we had no idea what the scale of the tumour was and how complex any treatment might be. We also made a very useful deal not to overdo the internet-trawling. As journalists, both of us knew how tempting it would be to log on and spend hours going through every site and web forum, regardless of how dodgy it looked. Every time I thought about the notion of taking chemotherapy drugs voluntarily while pregnant, my heart skipped a beat. In fact my heart skipped a beat just thinking about surgery with the baby. An anaesthetic is a very strong form of sedative and the idea that I would be having it in two days' time deeply upset me. The word 'anaesthetic' was traumatising enough, and the prospect of adding chemotherapy drugs to that mix was paralysing. It sounded wrong on every level, but maybe that was what Ann O'Doherty had been hinting at the other day.

She had begged us not to rush into any decisions until we had all the facts, and maybe this was why. She had known that we would be presented with the option of doing chemo during the pregnancy and that it would floor us: she had wanted us to be prepared for the jolt. I kept shaking my head in disbelief. Chemotherapy and pregnancy? I couldn't understand how that would work.

The following afternoon, I arrived at Kim's door and spent hours with her discussing the situation. We were obsessively going over the details and trying to get a handle on what was happening. We joked about people we had heard talking about cancer, and how you would hear that so-and-so had been brought in for surgery, but when they had opened him up, they'd found his cancer was so bad that they'd closed him right back up again. We fell around the kitchen, laughing at that.

'Riddled' was another word we bandied about. Jesus, imagine if I was 'riddled' with it? Instant tears were the result of that thought as our mood ranged from hilarity to disbelief. We were scared, though. All of us. We were so numb with worry that we could hardly tell what hour of the day it was. Every so often we would stop talking and just sit there staring at each other in silence. Then one of us would start again and it was always the same thing: 'But how ... how how how how?'

How?

At that stage, the word defined my life.

How?

And every conversation came back to the same place: how would a baby survive this treatment?

How would I?

The next day was Thursday, the day of the lumpectomy, and John had taken the day off work so he could accompany me to the hospital. He had told work about our situation and they were extremely supportive. Oisín was with my mum for the day and John's parents were going to take him that evening if John wanted them to. We had no idea how the day would pan out and, apart from John's boss and our immediate family, still no one else knew our news. I had decided that I needed the results from the first operation before I told the world. I felt I needed to know exactly what was happening to us and what our plans were before we discussed it with everyone. I was feeling sick to my stomach with nerves but I kept reassuring John that I was fine. I told him that this was the easy bit: all I had to do today was turn up. In the world of our five-minute strategy, today was manageable, I argued. First, park the car in the hospital car park. Then check in at Reception. Find the ward. Change into a gown. Get a needle, or a 'cannula', as I learnt to call it, inserted in the back of my hand so that they could give me the anaesthetic. Wake up after the anaesthetic and go home. Easy.

I checked in with Reception and was shown to my ward. I hopped into bed and Denis stuck his head around the door to reassure us about the plans for the procedure. John pulled up a chair beside me and we ploughed through a pile of magazines, trying to stay calm and cool. Around eleven a.m. the porters came to get me for stage one of the procedure. Sentinel-node mapping.

A jumble of thoughts was floating through my mind as I lay in the most spectacular, heartbreakingly sterile room imaginable in the nuclear zone of the hospital. It looked like a set from a futuristic movie. My mind was in turmoil when Ann O'Doherty appeared beside me. She had tracked me down to assure me that she had confirmed with the hospital's chief medical officer that they would be using the minimal radioactive dose possible for my procedures that day. I had not given it any thought other than that it was unavoidable. It hadn't occurred to me that they could work with the dosage and tailor it to each patient, which sounds really stupid now. Of course they can. Patients come in all shapes and sizes so they all require different drug levels. Ann had thought this through on my behalf and had ensured that every stage of my journey would be planned as carefully as possible. I was overwhelmed by her kindness, and her generosity with her time. It confirmed my instinct to trust the incredible medical team I had stumbled upon. I whispered, 'Thank you,' as she patted my head sympathetically.

She would be in touch, she said, and repeated her advice: 'No panic. No rush.'

The anaesthetist then appeared and inserted the dye.

This was the beginning. The first surgery. At this point I knew I was definitely going to be having at least one operation under anaesthetic, and chemotherapy would be next. I was so scared and feeling so powerless that I calmly decided to opt out of the whole thing for the day. I'd put my head in the sand and pretend that, far from being in a hospital in Dublin, I was on holiday far away from this madness. Sure, I was having sane, sober conversations with people but internally I was singing loudly, drowning the sound of my heartbeat as it threatened to burst through my skin. DUM DI DUM DUM, I hummed silently. I AM NOT REALLY HERE, I assured myself.

After a short while I was brought down to theatre, another cavernous, bleak moment. Saying goodbye to John and seeing the stress on his face was dreadful. He kissed me and clung to my hand, squeezing it tightly. Then the porters rolled my gurney away, leaving him bereft in the middle of the ward.

The nurses had told him to take a break and that they would call him when the surgery was finished so he decided go for a drive. Later he told me that that was when he fell apart. He sat screaming in the car, thumping the steering wheel. He was so desperately worried for us all and there was nothing he could do.

One of the most difficult things for John, I think, was the powerlessness. He is an extremely capable, competent man so for him to be relegated to the sidelines was awful.

Meanwhile I was having a ball downstairs in the operating theatre, once the drugs had kicked in. Denis' team of nurses were so friendly and helpful, and the views from the theatre across Dublin Bay were stunning. Ann's visit had given me a huge sense of reassurance and I felt I truly was in safe hands. I was chatting away happily to them, off my head, and then I was out cold.

Some hours later, when I woke up, John was beside my head and Clare Glenane was on the other side. Because of the pregnancy they offered me nothing stronger than paracetamol for the pain. Chemo was OK but I couldn't have morphine. Cruel. Clare explained to me that Denis had performed a lumpectomy and had taken sample nodes. I would stay in overnight, then be discharged and we would return the following Thursday for the results.

My right breast was tightly bandaged and there was nothing for me to do but lie there and get through the night. On paracetamol.

Oisín was staying with his grandparents and they had offered to drop him home the following day around tea time. You have to remember that at this point, as I was still on maternity leave, we had no formal childcare in place. Before the diagnosis disrupted things, the plan had been to start Oisín in the crèche when I returned to work in October but suddenly we needed him minded a lot and were having to rely on family.

I seemed to spend the next few weeks on the phone, constantly arranging pickups and drop-offs for him. Every single time we asked John's parents, my mum or my sister to take him they were more than willing. The family back-up and support we had was amazing and it has often occurred to me how much more difficult things would have been if our families had been down the country and we hadn't had that support so close by.

I have heard of cancer support centres around the country where patients are offered house-cleaning services and chauffeur back-up, both of which are incredibly important. Living with cancer is a brutal business, and while your world is collapsing around you, the dinner still has to be made. Regardless of how severe your diagnosis is, clothes must be washed, and if you can't do it, someone has to.

With the lumpectomy done and the lab analysing my lymph nodes, we were caught up in the waiting game. The next morning, after a broken night's sleep, we left the safety of my ward and headed back into the world. We were due to return the following week for the results so we headed out the door with my right breast tightly bandaged and an armful of information about how to manage washing myself over the next few days.

I felt quite calm now that the surgery was over and decided that I would do my best to fill the days until I had to be back at the hospital by going to the nicest places I could find for coffee dates.

With that in mind, we invited the family around for dinner on Saturday evening but it didn't quite go to plan. In fact, it was horrific. All day the ticker-tape had been flashing around and around my mind, and by Saturday night I was exhausted. I couldn't even think about cooking so we got a takeaway for around a dozen people and sat at our kitchen table. We started to eat and suddenly I felt sick. All the thoughts I had been banishing for the past forty-eight hours were bubbling up and threatened to erupt. What if the cancer was so advanced they had to tell me I was going to die? I could be dead within weeks, I thought. You hear of that. You hear of people getting a diagnosis and dying within weeks of it. What if it happened to me?

I was sitting beside my mum and reached for her hand. She squeezed mine. My head fell on her shoulder as the tears began to form. I was sitting at the table with all the family around me, and as my crying grew louder, I realised I was in pain, but not physical pain. No, this pain was different. It was mental pain, a kind of torture that I could almost taste. I was struggling to breathe sitting there. I felt like I had fallen into an abyss of deep, morbid pain. I was gulping air. I felt like the table had upended and I was clinging to it. My mind was whipping me, thrashing me, like a stick with nails in it, flaying the skin. *You are going to die*, the ticker-tape screamed at me. *You will never see these people again. You will have terminal cancer. It will have spread everywhere.*

Everyone carried on politely chewing and ignored my crying. I was whimpering, in agony, terrified, absolutely petrified. I was so scared. Every bone, every muscle hurt. The wolf was at the door, staring in at us. Saliva hung from his jaws.

What if I die?

My mum soothed me, talking me down, calming me. 'It was only a little spot,' she said. 'There are no lumps. It's going to be fine.' She continued to murmur comforting words into my ear over and over again.

'I'm going to die,' I moaned. She kept murmuring to me calmly, and I slowly, slowly started to settle down. The ticker-tape paused for a minute and I collapsed back on to my chair. 'I can't do this!' I wanted to shout. 'I cannot possibly do this! It's too damn hard and too horribly frightening. Someone, please, wave a magic wand and make it better. Take it all away. I can't bear it.'

As my mind raced, I realised that part of the panic was because the realisation was forming that I had no choice.

I *had* to bear it. That was my job.

I had many roles now. I was pregnant, and a patient and a mother. I had to stay in control and try to fill the days somehow until all this was resolved. All I could do was prepare for the next appointment and the one after that. Suddenly I was a full-time patient. My maternity leave was over. It had ended the minute Denis told me my diagnosis, so now I had a burden and I had to carry it. Somehow I had to learn to stumble on.

But how was I going to fill the endless hours ahead of me that summer? How was I going to survive today and tomorrow and the day after and the day after that and not go out of my mind with worry and fear? I had no idea.

In the end it was simple.

We employed our five-minute strategy.

Back in the kitchen at the horrendous meal, John came rushing over to me and whispered, 'It's fine. You're here with us, we all love you and nothing can happen to you in the next five minutes. You're safe. Get through the next five minutes and then we'll talk.'

I started to breathe again, and he was right: after five minutes, I had returned to some normality and was getting stuck into my curry and that was the beginning of my understanding of how the mind copes with this kind of overwhelming situation. Your mind rises and it falls. I remembered this from grieving for my father. Some days I would be fine and other days I would be doing some simple task, like making a cup of tea, when the blackness would overwhelm me and I would think, How can I do this? This is horrendous. I love him, I miss him and it's too hard to live with this pain. When Dad died, I was starting out on my career, taking those precious first steps into adulthood and to lose him at that point when our relationship was about to move from 'Dad, can you give me some cash?' to 'Dad, let me pay for this,' was cruel. To lose a parent as a child is, of course, horrific and, yes, it's different for adult children, but for any adult, to lose one of the few people who loves you unconditionally as you try to negotiate the maze of adult life is terribly lonely and sad.

Somehow, though, you muddle through. The mind creates an ebb and flow that allows you to survive. My mind did that when I lost my father, then did it again when I was starting to deal with my diagnosis. It had a terrible situation to process so it began with a ticker-tape to start me getting used to the language in my new world order. Then it began to plant seeds. It dropped the word 'cancer' in every now and then. Luckily you still need to eat and drink, and at moments when you think you cannot go on, in the midst of the pain and the panic, you suddenly find yourself thinking, God, I'm hungry, I'd love a bag of chips. So you stop, buy the chips, and that's another five minutes filled and that is how I filled the days. Five minutes by five minutes. Never thinking beyond the next five minutes. If possible.

It didn't always work, of course. Darkness was ready to leak into my mind at any opportunity. I was quickly learning that this was not a battle against cancer. This was a battle for my mind. The language we use around cancer is so competitive yet is entrenched in us now. People talk about 'beating' cancer and bravely 'fighting' it in a way that they do not associate with any other disease. You don't tell people who have been diagnosed with heart disease that they have to be brave and battle it. No. You say, 'I hope you have a great doctor and good luck with the treatment.' The same is true of cancer. 'Winning' against cancer is not an option. The moment you are diagnosed, it has 'won', so it is a ridiculous concept. Instead you try to deal with it and the only battle you can possibly engage in is the battle for your sanity in the middle of all the grimness.

Let me describe the battle.

You get a cancer diagnosis. You hope it has a good outcome and you rely on your medical team to make it all go away.

They are the ones fighting it.

You have no weapons except for how you deal with it emotionally and mentally.

Medical treatment is what cures the disease and that, mixed with a large truckload of luck, is your best plan. End of battle.

Your one precious tool is that you can control how you think about it so if you can keep positive about it at all, it really does help your mood and those around you. Everyone around you is drowning at those times, and as the reality of our situation began to sink in, I tried to be positive for me and for my family. I am certainly no Pollyanna, though, and was endlessly grumpy during the treatment, but when I remembered, I tried hard to be someway upbeat for at least part of the day and it usually made me feel a little better.

So, following the surgery, we just plodded on, breaking our days up into five-minute segments. I avoided the internet at all costs and John swears he did the same but I don't believe him for one minute. I drank gallons of coffee in every coffee shop in a twenty-mile radius and I ate cake. Lots and lots of cake. Somehow we had to get through to Thursday morning when we would return to St Vincent's to get the results from Denis. John worked on Monday and Tuesday but suggested that we should take Wednesday off and spend a day together before we faced into Thursday's appointment. Bright and early on Wednesday morning we packed up the car and headed off to Powerscourt Gardens, just the three of us. We parked the buggy in the Japanese garden, at a beautiful spot, and then we collapsed into each other's arms. We admitted that we were terrified and that both of us saw the world as black, black, black. We sobbed uncontrollably, and other visitors kindly steered away from the slightly mad-looking couple, with their cute baby in the buggy.

That night was my worst since the whole nightmare began. I was mentally exhausted from all the worry and strain. I am usually a fairly positive person. I can generally extract good things from bad moments and do not enjoy moaning, so I was finding it terribly frightening to be endlessly confronted with that boulder of bad news.

The bloody diagnosis was changing me, transforming me, and I hated it. Where had the joy gone? How could I not work this dilemma out? What was happening to me that I could see only one outcome from the meeting the next day and it was resolutely negative? Why was I convinced that I was going to die? Why was I so sure that Denis would tell me the cancer had spread everywhere and was inoperable? I sat in our kitchen, devastated. I was sure that I would lose the baby and life would end. I felt like the world was telling me, in the clearest terms possible, that it did not want my little family. The wolf was back and he was in the room, nibbling at the end of the bed and I shook and trembled for hours. I couldn't see hope anywhere. Even my body was reacting. The area around my breast and armpit where Denis had operated was suddenly more painful and the Steri-strip bandages that were slowly peeling off in the shower were itching like crazy. I felt ridiculous. Pregnant with cancer. How stupid was I?

The next morning, dawn eventually broke and we got ready to return to the hospital for the results of my surgery. John made me rehearse the script for the meeting with Denis over and over. He warned me that there would not be a movie moment when Denis came running into the car park, shouting, 'Everything's great – it was just a cyst after all!'

Instead we had to practise. John played Denis.

'Now, when we enter, Denis will shake our hands and

ask us to sit down. Then he will ask you to go and get undressed so that he can examine your breast. He will check the wound, but he will say nothing as he returns to his desk. He will then wait for you to dress before speaking so make sure you're wearing a simple top because I don't want to collapse again! Then you'll join us at the desk and he will go back over your history. Only then will he give you the results. OK?'

OK, OK, I get it.

We crawled into St Vincent's. My heart was hammering so loudly that I was sure people beside us in other cars and passers-by could hear it. What would Denis say to us? What had the surgery revealed and how many lymph nodes would be cancerous? Clare, our breast-care nurse, came to get us from Reception and we made small talk as she ushered us quickly into Denis' room. He jumped up to greet us, warm and friendly. But that means nothing, I warned myself.

Denis does not speak in long sentences. Professor John Crown who we are to meet shortly after this is the loquacious one. Denis speaks in short, staccato sentences so you hang on to every word as none are wasted.

'Evelyn, can I take a look at you?' he asks after quick hellos.

I nodded and stepped over to the bed, winking at John, who smiled back at me. Just as we had practised. John was giving a good impression of a calm man, but as Denis was checking my bandages, I could tell that my husband was nonchalantly trying to peer at Denis' notes on his desk. The folder was closed over though, so he was reduced to rubbing his chin furiously to keep himself calm. He was as anxious as I was, but somehow he managed to keep smiling and winking supportively at me.

Denis finished checking me and there was silence in the room as I hastily got dressed. This time it took me about ten seconds as I had planned my outfit with care. We didn't have long to wait. I had barely done up my last button and rushed over to the chair when he said, 'We got it all. The tumour. We got it. It was about half an inch long. It was an Invasive Ductal Carcinoma, Grade II – about 15mm in size.' He showed us with his fingers. Tiny. The size of a small coin.

The mood in the room was transformed. The difference between the atmosphere on Diagnosis Day and today was extraordinary. Even Denis was smiling. John and I had our hands clasped together and we were beaming. 'Now,' he went on to caution, 'I removed six lymph nodes and we did find a marker in one of the lymph nodes so we'll be doing an axillary node clearance.'

A marker? An axillary node clearance? What did that mean for me?

I quickly found out that tumour markers (also known as biomarkers) are substances found at higher than normal levels in the blood, urine or body tissue of some people with cancer. Although cancer cells often produce tumour markers, healthy cells produce them as well so that is why they need to be tested. Markers are helpful as they can confirm the diagnosis, assist your doctor to predict your cancer's behaviour and, most importantly, your possible response to treatment, as well as your chance of recovery. So, in my pedestrian world, it meant that there was something in my lymph nodes. A suggestion of cancer. Enough that we would need more surgery but, let's be honest, not a death sentence.

Slowly I realised that John had tried to prepare me for the axillary node clearance during the days leading up to this appointment. For a man who swore he hadn't researched it on the web, he seemed to be terribly well informed that the next step would probably be axillary node clearance, the medical term for the removal of the lymph nodes from the armpit. You need a general anaesthetic for this operation and you stay in hospital for four to seven days. Having the lymph nodes removed from the armpit is an important part of your treatment for breast cancer because, if the nodes aren't there, the chance of the lymph system passing cancerous cells on around the body diminishes. John had told me that it was likely there might be something and that I should be prepared to lose the lymph nodes, but that seemed OK to me. I was convinced that that was no big deal. The day before I had checked with a colleague of mine who had had cancer and she assured me that losing your lymph nodes was fine. Yes, you could get a bit of swelling and it meant that you couldn't have back massages any more as you couldn't risk overloading your remaining lymph glands with too much fluid, but she reckoned we didn't really need the nodes. When you're facing cancer, what's a few nodes? Doctors will wince at that, of course, but civilians have weird opinions on their bodies. If the lymph nodes had to go, then that was fine with me.

Denis went on to explain to us that performing an axillary clearance is the 'standard gold practice' so he was recommending that I had the operation. Gold practice is another term for best practice. He was taking maximum precautions with me, based on the results from the surgery, and I found that incredibly reassuring. Now that he had given us great news, I was happy to go ahead. 'Lymph nodes,' I snorted. 'Who needs them? Take 'em all out. I don't care.'

Up until that week, I hadn't even known that lymph nodes existed so I was happy to wave bye-bye to them, which seems incredible in retrospect. A fascinating aspect of this whole experience, which occurred to me after the treatment, is how quickly one is prepared to go under the knife having received a cancer diagnosis. If you had told me on the morning of my diagnosis that within a few hours I would be merrily offering to have my whole breast removed, not just a lump, I would have found this shocking. But here I was, in the space of two weeks, confidently writing off bits of my body in return for a clean bill of health. I suppose I was so focused on trying to survive the nightmare that I would do anything the doctors recommended. I felt lucky to have escaped a mastectomy. The more minor option, the lumpectomy, seemed like an OK deal at that point, which is now upsetting to me but at the time seemed very manageable. It meant that my right breast would be smaller than the left, but with a bit of padding in my bra I was sure that would be fine. I was unbelievably sanguine about it all. Years ago, I would most certainly have had a mastectomy: perhaps that was what made me feel a little bit lucky. I was only having a lumpectomy. So, you lose a nipple and part of your breast but what have you really got to complain about?

That is how strange this whole world gets. You can start to feel lucky for the most depressing of reasons. And they can always tattoo a nipple back on in the hospital.

I. Am. Not. Kidding.

Cancer sharpens everyone's focus. Nothing is blurry when you are making decisions to do with treatment. You want it out of your body NOW and whatever it takes to achieve that is fine.

Nipple going, no biggie. Lymphs, no problem. And what about chemotherapy? No problem. Suddenly you're bargaining with your body and you think, Hair, yup, I can lose that. Eyebrows, no one will notice. Toenails, it's winter, it won't matter.

A cancer diagnosis is so powerful that it instantly allows you to discard intimate parts of yourself without a second thought. Amputation doesn't even cross your mind. You just want it removed. Of course this sounds brutal but, in some ways, those decisions are the easy part.

In truth, the assault course is just beginning.

But we were allowed to enjoy that day. After all the agony of the previous few days, it felt like we had been ushered back from a precipice and we felt, again, weirdly lucky. To be sitting there at all is, of course, horribly unlucky, but once a surgeon starts telling you that he got it all and it's manageable, you can't help but start to feel lucky. You realise how many people have sat in similar seats over the years and not been given anything like the news that you just have and you're so grateful. You feel like you have dodged a bullet and you're weak with relief.

We thanked Denis and Clare and left the room. We had hardly crossed into the corridor before John was on the phone to everyone, my mum, his parents, Kim, Colm and Brian, to tell them our wonderful news. We were going to be OK. In a year's time it would definitely be behind us. It would be a grim, bleak, tough year but we were to focus on the baby now and try to plan the next stage in the journey. For that we were going to meet our next consultant, and he would make quite an impression on us. Next stop was Professor John Crown. Gulp.

Chapter 8

A Quite Important Meeting

That night, after meeting Denis, I slept well for the first time. No wandering around the house like some weird banshee figure. No making tea at four twenty-eight a.m. No wolf. Just sleep. Delicious sleep.

A few days earlier, I had been asked to nominate an oncologist to oversee the chemotherapy side of my treatment, and when I went researching possible candidates, Professor John Crown's name came up repeatedly. I was told that he was, in no particular order, honest, tough, fair, a straight shooter. Oh, and also a genius. He sounded daunting, but when I sat down with a pen and wrote down all the qualities I would need in a doctor who was going to see myself and the baby safely through this nightmare, honesty, toughness and a genius were pretty much on my list too, so I asked to be added to Professor Crown's patient roster. He is now a senator, of course, but back in my day he was merely one of the country's leading oncologists.

The day before we were due to meet him, one of my oldest school pals, Emer Conlon, called up to visit Oisín and me at the house. It had been two weeks since the diagnosis, and I had been avoiding her and the rest of my friends since that news had broken. Now I resolved to tell her what was happening to us. Up to that point, we had been keeping the news to ourselves because we were so worried about the pregnancy. We knew that, once word spread, people would be extremely concerned for us and we wanted to be clear in our plans before we made them public. When I'd told her everything she was extremely shocked. She hugged me as tears formed in her eyes and was visibly relieved when I assured her that the results from Denis were looking good. Telling her that I was pregnant and being treated for breast cancer was surreal. She kept saying, 'OK, OK,' very calmly, but I saw utter confusion, then worry seep into her face. Seeing this old friend of mine reduced to just sitting there and having to listen to something horrible about us that she couldn't fix gave me another taster of what was to come in the following weeks as we began telling other friends about our situation. She hugged me tightly, then got up and brought Oisín out into the sunshine in the garden to sit quietly with him as our news began to sink in. We were both so sad that day. Not scared. Not worried. Sad.

But now that I had told my first pal, the medical world came calling and it was time to meet with Professor John Crown and find out about the chemotherapy. Was he going to be able to reassure us enough that we could go ahead with this vicious treatment during my pregnancy? I shuddered every time I thought of it.

It was Friday, 25 June, which was also the day of my long-awaited school reunion. It was shaping up to be a wonderful event. I had spent hours organising it, and in the middle of all the diagnosis drama I had kept digging furiously away at my invitations, trying to track down former classmates all over the country and abroad. It was a terrific distraction during those horrible weeks. At this stage, no one from school knew anything about my news except Emer. I had decided to wait to tell any other friends as I did not want it to be the talking point of the night with people I had not seen in many years. Also, it was supposed to be a fun night and the idea of discussing my shocking health situation was exhausting to me. No one was going to know that I was even pregnant at the reunion and that suited me fine. Anyway, who knew what would happen at our consultation with the professor? If he had more devastating news for us I would not even be attending the reunion. So my diary for Friday, 25 June looked like this:

1. Two p.m. Meet Professor John Crown.
2. Five p.m. Hair and makeup appointment for reunion.
3. Seven p.m. Arrive at reunion.

Everything hung on that two p.m. meeting!

My plan for the afternoon was simple. If the meeting with John Crown went well and we were happy with the treatment plan, I would head from St Vincent's to my hair and makeup appointment and get ready for the reunion. If the meeting was a disaster, I would go home and crawl into bed, making some feeble excuse for not attending. I had spent months tracking people down, and more than one hundred former school mates were due to descend on Vicar Street from eight o'clock to watch Dara Ó Briain perform and have a beer together afterwards. It would be odd for me not to be there but at that point my life was truly bizarre.

We had no idea what to expect. Sitting outside Professor Crown's office that afternoon, we were battle ready. I distracted myself by fielding texts from school pals about the arrangements for the night ahead, and John was answering work emails. The time crawled. We had lists and lists of questions with us, and as I read and then re-read them for the hundredth time, the speed at which all this was happening hit me forcefully again. We had only got our diagnosis two weeks ago and since then I had had my first surgery for my lumpectomy and the sentinel-node test.

It had been only two weeks, but there had been so many ups and downs in that tiny period. On the day of the diagnosis we had been so devastated, and then at our next appointment we had been buoyed up by the news from Denis that it was all looking good, but once that good news had sunk in, we were straight on to the next hurdle, another unknown: the treatment. Was it unavoidable? Would it affect our baby? What could we expect to happen?

In just two weeks, we had gone from civilian status to waiting-room experts. Here we were at another doctor's door, waiting for more unpredictable news. The whole thing was torturous. And as I sat there, all I wanted to do was to run into John Crown and shout, 'Can we do this? Tell me that we can do chemotherapy in pregnancy and this baby can be safe and I can be safe and promise me that this will all go away some day.' But, of course, it doesn't work like that, so we just sat there quietly, calmly, maturely, responsibly but, yes, a little impatiently.

There was so much to discuss with him that this meeting had the potential to run for hours. I was beginning to think that we had so many questions that we should just move into his room for the weekend. I looked at the list of questions and it struck me again how horrible they were. It still makes me queasy to think of them. I was seven weeks pregnant and this was my world now.

When other pregnant women were planning nursery designs and moaning about a bit of backache, we had to think about such charming things as: does chemotherapy increase the risk of miscarriage? What will be the additional risks to the baby? When will we know if the baby is affected? What kind of extra medical care will we get? How many anaesthetics can you safely have and carry a normal pregnancy?

As I sat there, the other word that had been stalking me for days struck me again. That horrible word 'abnormalities'. Surely you cannot pump toxic chemotherapy drugs into yourself without there being consequences for a baby. It did not make any sense. Abnormalities. How far were we willing to go if the baby might be affected in any way by this treatment? That was my darkest question. I knew that John had his own questions and would not leave the office until he got satisfactory answers. There was a lot of pressure on the two of us as we sat there quietly, absorbed in our thoughts.

The list of questions was certainly long and bleak, but at least it was deadly honest, and Professor John Crown sounded like a man who would respond to honesty.

It was ten minutes past two and we were all geared up for him, when he suddenly appeared in Reception and warmly invited us into his office. We needn't have worried.

John Crown is extremely tall, charismatic and charming, he has a booming, confident voice with more than a hint of an American accent so his presence fills any room he enters. He introduced himself and almost immediately set about examining me thoroughly. I liked his style straight away. I undressed quickly and lay back while he poked and prodded and I found that the confident way he dealt with me from those first minutes made me feel very safe in his care.

'OK, no lumps there,' he pronounced. Fair enough.

This was a procedure I would get used to over the months ahead. He would press all the way around my torso and then state baldly, 'OK, nothing there.' And the way he said it always left me in no doubt that if he had found anything he would have told us instantly. No punches pulled. He has since told me that one of the issues he wanted to confront when he started treating patients was the secrecy around cancer. His decision to be open and honest with patients has contributed hugely to the normalisation of the disease that we now expect here in Ireland, which is to be welcomed.

I dressed and returned to the chair.

'So,' he said. 'You are pregnant and you need treatment.'

I nodded nervously. It was beginning. We would be here for hours thrashing this out, I thought, and clenched my hands.

'That's fine. I have been successfully performing chemotherapy on pregnant women for many years now. My first Irish chemotherapy baby is now a happy, healthy fifteen-year-old. I usually deal with one to three cases a year. After twelve weeks, chemotherapy drugs do not breach the placenta wall, so we will wait until you are safely into your second trimester and the placenta wall is in place and then we will begin. Does that make sense?' he queried.

We both just nodded mutely.

He grabbed a calendar. 'OK, let's discuss time frames. You will be fourteen weeks pregnant in the week of the sixteenth of August so we will start that Tuesday, the seventeenth. You will have six doses of chemotherapy, one every three weeks. Your hair will fall out completely twelve to fourteen days after your first treatment. Every single hair will go – don't think it won't, so be prepared. You will be wearing a wig at Christmas but your hair will have grown back by Easter. You will have the baby in February and then you shall get your radiotherapy. You should be done by the start of next summer, but you need to confirm all this with your radiotherapy consultant. So, I imagine you have many questions, so let's begin.'

John and I gulped. Right. Em. Well, yes, actually, just a few, since you ask.

I began. 'What are the risks—'

I didn't even get to finish the question.

'What are the risks to the baby? Normal miscarriage levels are 1.5 to 2 per cent. Your treatment increases that risk by 1 per cent. I haven't lost a baby yet. Unfortunately one of my colleagues has but it is rare. Additionally, you may want to know about foetal abnormalities. Well, there is no increased risk of foetal abnormality.'

I stuttered, 'I j-j-just find it so hard to believe that we

can have chemo and that the baby will be fine. How is that possible?'

He looked straight at me and then his tone of voice softened: 'Evelyn, it is possible because we know what we're doing. We have done it many times and it has been successful – I promise. My secretary Anastasia has photos out there on her desk of babies who have been through this, and they are happy, smiling, healthy kids. Trust us. The placenta wall keeps the baby safe while you are having the treatment. We know this works.'

I was a bit stunned by his honesty, but then I thought, Well, you did ask.

Now it was John's turn. He cleared his throat. I suddenly realised that this was his big question, his version of my abnormalities question. I had been so worried about uttering the words out loud that it was a relief for it to be done and now it was his moment.

'Professor, I just have one thing that I need you to talk to me about.' He paused. I looked over at him as he cleared his throat. 'I need to know that Evelyn is going to get the best care, and that even though she is pregnant, her care is not going to be comprom—'

John Crown stopped him. 'John, if you're asking – which I think you are – if you are asking me if we will, in any way, modify Evelyn's treatment because she is pregnant you have nothing to fear. I treat the mother. That is my job. You have a small child at home, I believe.' We nodded. 'Well, in my view there is no point in having two healthy babies and no mother to care for them. I am very clear on this point. We will treat Evelyn like any other patient presenting with her situation. Now, I know there is a lot to absorb there for the two of you so while we are here, feel free to ask me anything. Is there anything else you would like to raise?'

A few bits and pieces, nothing major, and we were done. Somehow this man had trodden a path through our worst nightmares and demonstrated to us that there was light somewhere beyond the grim world which had been consuming us for two weeks now. His confidence in his medical team's ability to look after us and our tiny baby changed night into day for us. This could happen. This might actually work. We picked up our things and started smiling as we thanked him. When we were back out in Reception I checked the clock and it was two twenty-five p.m.

Turning to each other, John smiled at me. 'Do you think you're going to make your hair appointment so?'

'Em, actually … yes, I think so.'

'Good,' he replied, and hugged me. We paid for the parking, then wandered back to our car to get ready for the reunion. It had been the most extraordinary meeting of my life.

Chapter 9

Operation Disclosure

Bagels, bagels and more bagels. Thai takeout. I could recite the takeaway menu by heart. John and I were living on them. We couldn't make any decisions. Sometimes, we needed to double-check that we were actually dressed when we left the house. It was chaotic. We were also facing the inevitable question of when we were going to tell everyone. We had discussed the John Crown meeting over the weekend and had decided it was a simple choice: follow his plan or flounder. We had no other options and he had been extremely convincing so we hugged each other and decided to go for it. We finally had clarity. At this point though my moods were fluctuating wildly. Some moments I felt strong and focused, and even practical about it all, and other times, mainly when the day slipped into night, I would feel cross and scared and would lie limp with worry on the couch. Ultimately, what saw me through that time was John Crown's confidence. He could do this. He had done this. We would do this. We would go ahead with both the pregnancy and the chemotherapy treatment. Gulp.

The school reunion had been fun. Apparently. I was gone by one a.m. but I am told that it had gone on until the small hours when the last gang was standing outside Vicar Street singing the Ó Riada Mass from our school days, which is always the sign of a good night out, I think. I had floated around slightly detached from the whole thing.

Anyway, now the reunion was over I had one job left. I had been invited to do a screen test as a potential presenter for a new RTÉ daytime TV programme on that Monday morning. I decided to go ahead with the audition, which sounds absolutely crazy but it meant a lot to me. Obviously, even if I got offered the job, I wouldn't be able to take it but I wanted one last normal work day. I greedily wanted one more fun experience before the grimness of treatment took over. The deal I made with John was that I would do the audition in the morning and we would start telling people my news that afternoon. It was getting tougher to keep it to ourselves, and now we knew what our plan was for the summer, it was time to start bringing people in on it. With that plan in place, I headed off to the audition for one last grasp at normality.

It went well, I think. I really enjoyed myself and totally forgot about all that was happening in my life at that moment. I had surreal chats with researchers about topics and news stories of the day and I was totally engaged with the show. This felt like me. The real me. It was fantastic. Presenting a programme live, with the red lights on, is something I always, always enjoy. There is an adrenalin rush to broadcasting live, but also the knowledge that when you're on the mic, nothing matters at that moment than doing the best programme you can. The passionate discussions with fantastic producers and researchers before a show and the post-match analysis afterwards were equally important and interesting to me. Standing there that day, checking my script, I was reminded of how much I enjoy that whole world.

Then it was over.

The screen test had ended, they thanked me and then it was time for me to go. I blinked hard. I looked around at the crew, many of whom I had known over the years, and said goodbye as I moved towards the door. They called goodbye back to me and waved, saying we'd catch up in the canteen in the weeks ahead. I nodded and continued smiling. They had no idea that I was saying goodbye to so much that morning. I was saying goodbye to a possibility, and goodbye to a past. Once I walked out of that door, and made my way into the RTÉ offices in Donnybrook to talk to people, everything would be different. Right now I was one of them, one of the crew. In a few short hours, I would become a full-time patient.

I felt calm, though. I like order, and now we had order and clarity. Denis had confirmed that the cancer had not spread, which was the most important bit, and at least we were on a path now. There was a roadmap, and I adore roadmaps. I like the feel of them in my hand, and I like having a timetable, a tour guide and paperwork. They reassure me.

So, our next job was to tell people. I got into my car and drove to Donnybrook. Once I had found parking outside the radio centre, I rang John and we kick-started 'Operation Disclosure'. We had split up our list of people we had to tell. He spent the afternoon calling some of our closest colleagues and friends into his office and broke the news. I was using my car as my office!

The first person I called was my old pal Ann Marie Power. I told her that I was outside the radio centre so she should grab us some coffees and hop into my car for a minute for a quick chat. She said it all sounded very mysterious but that she would be out shortly. She emerged a few minutes later and I waved her in. She clambered into the passenger seat, handed over my coffee and I took a deep breath. I had TV hair and makeup on so looked vaguely glamorous, which seemed ludicrous considering what we were about to discuss.

While she was admiring my locks, I put up my hand to

stop her. 'I have something to tell you,' I said. John and I had worked out a script that we would use. She was my first experiment.

'I have good news and some terrible news but bear with me because it all works out in the end and it's going to be fine.'

Her eyes widened but she just said, 'OK, right. What is it?'

And I said, 'I'm pregnant again, which is wonderful news …'

'Yes,' she said. 'Wow! Whe—'

I stopped her. 'I also have dreadful news, sweetheart – oh, Ann Marie, I have breast cancer. Sorry – I *had* breast cancer but it's all gone now. So the next step is preventive treatment and it's going to work out fine, they tell us, but it's very scary…' As I babbled on, doing very badly with the perfect script John and I had worked out, I could see tears form in her eyes.

'Jesus, I wasn't expecting this,' she said. 'Poor you …'

'I know, I know, it's a lot to take in, it's dreadful, but we really are feeling optimistic about the whole thing.' And just as I was about to kick in to a load of detailed answers about the whole situation, I spotted another pal, Sandra Byrne, coming towards me with tears running down her face. She had been on John's list but had seen me. Ann Marie and I got out of the car.

'John just told me. Oh, God, oh, God, are you going to be OK?' She hugged me fiercely. I stood in the RTÉ car park with those two good friends of mine wrapped around me and thought, Christ, how did we get to this?

Now we had started the ball rolling, I needed to get home to start calling people and so for the next two days, John and I spent our time counselling people and mopping up their tears. We were so used to the news by then that we could absolutely understand the confusion for everyone when we told them. Telling people was horrendous because you could hear the stress in their voices, the worry, the concern. Some phone calls stand out – my old pal Michael Parke in London, for example. We had missed each other's calls all day and by the time I got him he told me he knew it had to be bad news. Another person I was dreading telling was my dear friend Elayne Devlin. She was away on holidays with her family and I didn't want to disturb her there. Of course, when she returned a week later, she was furious with me for not ringing her and Mike, her husband, to tell them. Yet another great friend of mine, Aoileann Farley, whom I had known since I was two, was wonderful when I told her and promised she would support us all the way. To prove it, by tea time she had delivered a pot of curry for our dinner. But it wasn't just her. The rest of her family were amazing as well, as were all my friends. It knocked me for six.

The one aspect of it all that floored me was how everyone tried to focus immediately on the pregnancy and tell us how happy they were for us. I asked people, when they were discussing this with their partners or friends, to emphasise that we were thrilled with the pregnancy and that that was the most important thing. And they did. For days, weeks and months afterwards I had cards and letters from distant pals and I was always impressed with how people would mention the pregnancy first, and congratulate me about that rather than writing dirges about the diagnosis. They were extremely sensitive and subtle in their handling of the cancer part of the story.

I am still sensitive around that word myself and I've had the bloody thing. You may even notice that I do not use the word 'cancer' a lot. I do not bandy the word around. I use the term 'diagnosis'. 'Cancer' is a desperate word, not something that anyone would invite casually into their world so I do not either. And I carried the marks of it on me: while the bandages on my breast were slowly peeling away, there were still a few there so I had not yet seen what my breast looked like post-surgery. Apart from some tenderness around the surgical site, though, I was not experiencing any pain. I was officially sick but, in many ways, had never felt better. How could I be a patient when I was generally feeling fine and looking grand? I would sit at my dressing table and just stare at my reflection, like some corny scene from a depressing French movie. I would gaze at my bandaged breast and wonder how it would look when the bandages finally peeled away. Then I would suddenly remember I needed to purée some carrots for Oisín and snap out of it.

In the weeks after we'd broken the news, everyone told me that it took them days to get their head around our situation. Many of my friends have had children yet had never heard that it was possible to have chemotherapy in pregnancy. Standing in my kitchen the day after we had started telling people, reading pages and pages of loving emails, I realised that the idea of my having chemo was the most shocking part of our news, so I resolved there and then that I would try not to over-analyse that aspect of it. I had asked my questions, John Crown had answered them, and all I wanted to do now was to enjoy this pregnancy as much as I had done my first. I told myself that I would concentrate on the baby and John Crown could worry about the rest.

And that worked for five minutes. It was hard to feel anything other than loved and supported that week as the letters and emails flooded in, though. Over and over again I was told about countless people who were lighting candles for us in churches all over Ireland and saying novenas for us. I found that kind of interest from complete strangers, in some cases, unbelievably moving and, yes, it helped. It all helped. Every letter, every phone call, every quiet word passed on. People were so kind and discreet. In fact, only one person wrote a stupid message on my public Facebook wall: 'Sorry to hear about your cancer. Hope you feel better soon.' It kind of made me laugh.

Chapter 10

Complications

Now the word was out about my situation, at least among my close family and friends, life became much easier. We could stop fobbing people off with lame excuses about why we were suddenly not around to make plans. We were visible again, and I was able to celebrate my pregnancy publicly, which was lovely. I was nearly ten weeks pregnant and my body had embraced it enthusiastically, with a bump beginning to show already. (Well, I could see it!) It was still very early but from now it would be back on with the old maternity leggings and vests and out with the skinny jeans.

I felt great and was feeling very positive about the pregnancy. I was due back in the hospital a week later for my axillary clearance operation in which Denis would remove more lymph nodes from my armpit. I spent my last precious few days off meeting up with friends and family. At that point, I was feeling calm and in control and I realised that until then I had been living on that weird adrenalin that kicks in during a time of crisis. The fact that we had been sneaking around so furtively had greatly added to the pressure on us, so it was good to be able to chat to friends openly. At midday, when the sun was out and the day was bright, I felt strong, clear-headed and optimistic. At midnight I was so tired and spent that I would fall into bed and go straight to sleep. During that time I managed to stop overthinking for a few days. Maybe it was the pregnancy or just exhaustion from the trauma of the earlier weeks, but for the first time since the diagnosis I was able to sleep. It was a relief.

After that little break at home, I now had to build myself up for the axillary clearance operation. My anxiety began to grow as I faced into another surgery and more general anaesthetic. I reminded myself, however, that I was absolutely confident in the hospital staff's handling of my pregnancy so it should all be fine. Sometimes that calmed me but not always. This poor baby, I thought. They had already endured one operation and now we were facing into a second. I felt terrible because the baby was being so co-operative and I hadn't experienced a single moment of discomfort from the pregnancy. They really, really did not deserve any of this, I fumed.

The night before the surgery, John packed my bag, then lifted Oisín into our bed for comfort and we held each other tight. The next morning, before we handed him over to Peigí, I hugged the baby for ages. I knew I was going to be in hospital for a few days this time, so was not sure when I would see him next, although I had made everybody promise that they would bring him in as soon as possible. He was just seven months old and as gorgeously cute as ever. He smiled and gurgled at me, and I kissed him again and again before handing him over and getting into the car.

We headed off yet again in the direction of St Vincent's Hospital. We knew the drill a little better this time, and as we checked in and were settled in my ward we distracted ourselves with magazines and papers. I changed into my theatre gown, kissed John goodbye and headed off to surgery feeling his love swaddled tightly around me. 'It will be fine,' he mouthed at me, smiling as the porters came to get me. All the reassurances in the world are lovely, but as I was being wheeled in for more surgery my heart was hammering again.

As I lay on the gurney, looking out at the spectacular views over Dublin Bay, Denis appeared, reassured me that everything was going to be grand, and then I was given the anaesthetic. Later, when I came around, I was back in the ward and there was now a soft, plastic drain inserted in my armpit. It had been explained to me that the drain was required because the operation suddenly removes the drainage system your lymph nodes offer and your body has to get used to dispersing the excess fluid itself. For the first few days they give you a drain to help set up the process. You have a thin plastic tube, about a foot long, hanging out from your armpit and it feeds into a soft tennis-ball-sized plastic sphere, which I pinned to my nightdress. Apparently the ball used to be made of really hard plastic, which made sleeping impossible. Envisage trying to sleep with a cricket ball under you the whole time! However, one of the consultants had been working in Canada where they used the softer plastic ball and she had introduced it into Ireland. I am mentioning it in passing as an example of one of those tiny developments that can hugely influence a patient's experience.

Managing the drain was a little odd at the start. I used to worry that it would get pulled out or snag on something, but Clare, the breast-care nurse, reassured me that they had inserted a substantial length of the tubing internally so I wouldn't pull it out. Now, she told me, I just had to recover from the surgery and relax.

This time, my hospital stay was nearly a pleasure. Visitors were constantly coming in and out, and my stack of magazines grew higher than a hairdresser's salon. It was late June and the weather was warm. The days were long and bright, and I remember that hospital stay with some affection. It had been nearly four weeks since I had first been diagnosed, and while my life had changed in so many ways, lots of things had stayed the same. I was still *me* in the middle of all this. I hadn't changed. I still liked company and found solace in conversation, and the nurses proved terrific allies in the days ahead. They were warm and friendly and I made a huge effort to get to know them as their stories of life on the outside helped buoy me up.

One afternoon my friend Emma McIvor arrived and we talked about what I could do once my hair started falling out during chemotherapy. I had been dreading this but, as is the way with close friends, Emma made it fun. She had brought some scarves along and we had a great laugh pinning them this way and that. I nearly forgot why I was there for a while. Until I had a phone call about that day's plans for Oisín when I was sharply reminded of how artificial the whole set-up was becoming.

Oisín was being minded on a strict rota system that involved Peigí, John's parents and our various siblings, who were all meticulous in their arrangements. I do not know how John managed it all while also running his office in work. He knew at every minute of every day who was picking Oisín up and where they were dropping him off, and my room became Oisín HQ, with people coming and going with him, swapping bags of clothes and nappy supplies. It was crazy but he seemed to be happy spending time with his grannies and cousins, and as he was eating and sleeping well, I had to comfort myself that he was doing fine.

It was a busy time. As the hospital was so near work,

many of my colleagues would land in to me, people like my old *Gerry Ryan Show* boss, Siobhan Hough, 'just popping in' for a quick visit and staying four hours. Our old radio pal Philip Boucher-Hayes was another 'quick visitor', who called in for a minute but left hours later, as did Deirdre Magee, another *Gerry Ryan Show* veteran who was amazingly supportive.

The bleakest moment of that hospital experience came after the second day when the last of my breast-surgery bandages came off in the shower. A nurse called Jackie sat with me as we peeled away the final stubborn bit. She held my hand as I looked down and saw my scar for the very first time.

'Oh,' I exhaled as I tried to take it in. 'Oh, so that's what it looks like. Wow. OK, right.'

She stroked my head gently. 'I know, sweetheart, I know. It's a shock but it's fine. It will be fine and the scar will fade in time.'

I just kept looking at the lump of skin that was unrecognisable to me now. My right breast was about a third smaller than it had been and now it had a neat but very visible scar running right across the middle. I was thirty-eight, yet my body was unfamiliar to me at that moment.

Jackie helped me dress again and wouldn't leave until I said I was OK. Eventually I let her go but as I fell back on the pillows I felt exhausted. I looked out of the windows at the stunning trees in Elm Park that formed such a beautiful backdrop to my hospital room and tried to rationalise what had just happened. My breast was changed. But there were options. The surgeons could work on it and improve it – but, really, did it matter? The trees outside the window truly were magnificent and seemed to stretch up into the sky endlessly. They gave me more comfort than I even realised at the time.

How many patients had they watched over down the years? How many others had been in that very room, as scared as I was, terrified about the future, looking out at those giants of nature for some sort of reassurance?

I had had breast surgery. That would never ever change, but then I thought, I have a baby to think of and they don't care how your breast looks, so get on with it today and we'll deal with this another day. Five minutes.

I could easily get through the next five minutes, I ordered myself, and at that moment the lunch trolley helpfully came along and I filled more than five minutes eating a delicious turkey and ham dinner.

John was constantly in touch. He was working away down in RTÉ and had his bike outside his office window so he could hop on it and visit me regularly in St Vincent's, so everything was ticking along.

A few days later, my drain and I were discharged with much advice on how to clean and manage the wound in my armpit. Luckily it was warm so I could wear vest tops to accommodate the new accessory in my life. I spent a few days pottering around the garden, with many friends dropping in to offer help and support. Many evenings we would discover a platter of lasagne or a casserole that someone had left for our dinner. Deborah Wiseman, an old pal from my Galway days, rang from outside the house one day to tell me that she didn't want to disturb me, but that she was leaving a curry on the doorstep for us. People were extraordinarily kind and it all helped.

Then one evening, about a week after the operation, and the night before we were due to return to Denis for the results, I was locking the back door when the black wolf suddenly reappeared at the corner of the house.

As I opened the door to take a closer look, he disappeared. Why was he back? Everything seemed to be going fine after the surgery and the drain was manageable, if uncomfortable. The phone was busy with people calling and texting and I was enjoying meeting friends and bringing Oisín out to the park in the sunshine so why would the wolf be back? I shook my head. I'm going to forget that, I thought. No more.

All my calmness dissipated the next day as we trekked back into St Vincent's to meet Denis for news on my axillary clearance tests. What if he had found cancer in all the lymph nodes he had removed? What were the implications of that going to be? I was starting to get really queasy. This time my sister had joined me and John for the appointment and, sitting outside Denis' office in the waiting area, I held one of their hands in each of mine. I leant my head on Kim's shoulder and together we tried to finish the crossword in a newspaper that had been left behind on the table. I realised how rattled I was when I struggled to spell 'lake'.

Every so often I would hear myself mutter, involuntarily almost, 'This is just another crappy day. We just file this as another horrible stage of all this.' They squeezed my hands. John was convinced that it was going to be fine and he smiled at me as Clare, the breast-care nurse, arrived to walk us down to Denis' office.

As soon as I stepped through the door, Denis was talking to me enthusiastically, and he assured me that he was very happy with how the surgery had gone. He explained to me that he had performed a level-two clearance, which meant that there were still a few lymph nodes left which would help with the fluid drainage in my arm in the future. Most importantly, no other marker cells had been found so I was definitely clear of cancer now. He even went so far as to say that he wished he could put the uninvolved nodes he had removed back in.

I could feel the relief flooding Kim and John, and I sat there grinning. Gone, gone, gone. Cancer was gone. Wow.

Denis had seen off the worst part of this whole nightmare and I shed a tear while still grasping Kim and John's hands. Big day. Big, happy, marshmallowy day.

Gone. My new favourite word. Technically I was in remission, but emotionally all I cared about was that wonderful four-letter word, GONE. Deleted. Past tense.

Over. Cancer gone. The mood in the room brightened and then, with everyone beginning to chatter happily, Denis headed off, with my profound thanks ringing in his ears. Denis, of course, would not have sat around and waited for thanks: not his style. Denis was off to the next patient. But I think I managed to grab a hug as he bolted out the door.

Anyway, Clare led me over to the bed in the corner and started to remove my drain. She seemed to be pulling what seemed like endless lengths of plastic tubing out from under my arm. It was nearly comical. She explained to me that, as there was now effectively a hole in my armpit, the importance of sterilising and cleaning the wound was key to my recovery.

I half listened. After all I had been through, I was not paying a huge amount of attention. All I cared about was that I was cancer-free and ready to move on to the next stage. I was ten weeks pregnant and now that we had this result from Denis I had nothing to focus on except the baby. Chemotherapy was not going to happen for another month so I had four weeks off to catch up on my baby scans and start really focusing on the pregnancy. Gone, gone, gone. What a beautiful word. Strong and elegant. And definite.

You don't mess with 'gone'.

John went back to work, and over the next two days I had a lovely time both playing with Oisín and making an appointment for our first baby scan.

When John came home from work on the Friday evening, we made some plans for the weekend and headed off to bed. The next day, Saturday morning, BAM! I woke up feeling dreadful.

I felt nauseous and incredibly hot. At first I thought that maybe I was finally getting morning sickness like any other mum-to-be so I was kind of pleased that some normal pregnancy symptom had kicked in. I told John I would stay in bed for a few hours, but I couldn't get any rest. One minute I was shivering with cold, and as soon as I pulled the quilt up around me I would be throbbing with heat. I felt like I was going to combust. I had a terrible, uncomfortable, restless day and couldn't eat. John was making soothing ginger tea to help settle my stomach but it wasn't working. At some point I fell into an agitated doze – one of those where you're thrashing around in the bed, half awake and half asleep. At some stage, I thought I could hear my sister Kim's voice in my dreams and then I slowly came around and realised I wasn't dreaming: I could definitely hear her and Norman downstairs chatting with John and Oisín.

It was another gorgeously warm day but I was lying in bed under the covers fully dressed with socks, jeans, t-shirt and a cardigan, and now my body was pumping sweat. I realised I was in serious trouble. My body was shaking and I just knew that I needed to get to the hospital – and fast. I had no idea what was wrong but I needed help urgently. I tried to call out to John downstairs but I couldn't raise my voice above a whisper. I was too weak. I fell back on the pillow, then tried again to call out to him, but even though I was roaring at him inside my head, I could barely register a whisper. Eventually I counted to ten and slowly crawled over to my mobile at the side of the bed and rang John, then Kim. John's phone rang beside me in the bed and Kim's rang out. I slumped back until I had regained a little strength. One last push, I thought. I rolled over the bed, gently fell to the floor, crawled over to the bedroom door and, using the last of my energy, called out, 'Joooohnnnn,' as loudly as I possibly could. I then fell back exhausted.

He came running up the stairs, took one look at me and asked Kim to grab the thermometer. It registered a temperature of 39 degrees so John bundled me up and rushed me into St Vincent's. I remember stumbling to our car, looking back and seeing Norman standing in our doorway holding Oisín, who was a whole seven months at this stage, and Kim carrying my bag out, assuring me that they would mind him for us.

We rushed into the hospital and went to A & E where we were admitted immediately. One of Denis' team was on duty that night and she did all my blood tests, then rang him for advice. I had developed an infection at the site of the drain. Because of the pregnancy, they would have to proceed very carefully with my treatment. They could not just shovel strong antibiotics into my system.

People often ask me what the low points of the whole

experience were. I have a top ten in my head and that night is right up there, fighting for number one. On my way into the hospital I was scared, but by the time I got there I felt so dreadful that I wasn't scared any more. I remember saying to John that I felt like I was going to die and that was fine because it would end the pain. I had gone beyond caring. I just wanted the misery to stop. My body was in trauma and I just wanted to float away.

To be reduced to that state was horrendous. Not to care any more, when all I had done for the previous month was fight a mental battle, seemed unimaginable but that was how sick I felt. I tried to muster up pictures of the family and remember all the love they surrounded me with but nothing mattered. I just wanted to be left alone so I could slip quietly away.

John just sat there rubbing my hand, reminding me how much he loved me and how much I had waiting for me at home. I tossed and turned, dementedly begging for painkillers. Anything to end the pain I felt. The team tried to reassure me but with the pregnancy they had to be careful. Slowly they started to give me medication and I felt a little better. I was admitted for the night into a four-bed ward. Because it was late I was quietly wheeled into the slot beside the door, and as I was still boiling hot, I remember staring at the window longingly, craving the beautiful cool air outside. I began to feel calmer, and urged John to go home and get some sleep. I told him I would call him in the morning and he could visit Oisín at Kim's before coming in to see me with fresh clothes. He left reluctantly but I waved him off and tried to settle down to sleep. I had a restless night, though, and my temperature was constantly monitored.

Very early next morning, I was extremely uncomfortable again and felt hot, hot, hot. Two of my favourite nurses, Jackie, who had looked after me when my breast bandage was removed, and Imelda, who had been there during my first visit for my lumpectomy and had constantly kept turning up to look after me, were there again for me, minding me, and it helped a lot. They stayed close beside me, battling to get my temperature down, but it was an impossible task. Every time they put a cold compress on my head or legs it would dry up with the heat from my body.

Another nurse, Breda, took my temperature. She paled. 'It's 41.3,' she gasped and then all hell broke loose as she rushed off to ring Denis. She later told me that after many years' working in a hospital she had never treated an adult whose temperature had exceeded forty degrees. Forty-one is extremely grave, and I was delirious from the heat of the infection and had no idea what was happening around me. Poor John arrived in the middle of this drama.

I had spoken to him earlier that morning and reassured him that I was fine so he was not to come in until around eleven a.m. When he arrived at my bedside he got a terrible shock when he heard about my temperature – one of the nurses muttered to him that you could die at

42 degrees. There was nothing he could do but look on as I was soaked in freezing cold cloths in vain attempts to bring my temperature down. This situation was so complex because of the pregnancy and they could not treat me with regular medication so it was a terribly tough morning for everyone involved. I could sense the tension in the room at times as the nurses fought to control my infection but at other times I had no idea where I was. I kept rambling and apologising to people for causing all this trouble as I writhed in agony on the bed. Suddenly a doctor called Myles appeared and explained that the situation had developed so dramatically that they were recommending an operation. They had no choice but to whisk me urgently down to surgery and remove the infection.

I turned in panic to John. Somehow the decision to operate had made it through to my fevered brain. Not another general anaesthetic! Please, no. That would mean our baby would have had to undergo three. How could a tiny baby survive such a trauma? 'Please, please, please, no,' I sobbed to John, but as my temperature was continuing to soar, he made it clear to me that we had no choice.

'The baby is in danger, they need to operate,' John told me. 'We need to do this and it will be fine. We are going to have to go to the operating theatre again but we have no choice,' he soothed me. The paperwork appeared for me to give permission for the operation to take place and

I knew then that this was really going to happen. John pointed out that they were going to take the same care with me as they had during the previous operations. They had worked out fine, hadn't they?

Had they?

I didn't know any more. I was still only ten weeks pregnant and was due to have my first scans the following week so I didn't really know if the pregnancy was still happening. It was horrendous. We were going to have to gamble again. I bent my head to sign yet another consent form. And then we were off. Still twisting and turning in pain in the bed, I was wheeled off to surgery. As the anaesthetist began his work, I lay in the now too-familiar operating theatre, took one last look at Dublin stretched out below me through the windows and then I was out for the count.

When I came around, I felt completely different.

Cool and calm. Luckily, I had been given my own room so once the drama had subsided I could just lie back and think. It had been a tough day. Breda dropped by to review it with me and that was when she blurted out how scared she had been. She was terrified for me because of the baby, and she said that all the nurses were thinking of me that night. Mum and Kim had rushed to join John by my bedside that afternoon and stayed with me right through the dark evening and, although I didn't know it at the time, they were exceedingly concerned. They thought we might lose the baby because the infection seemed out of control. They could not begin to see how myself and the baby would make it through this safely. Later both John and Kim told me that that day had been the most frightening since the diagnosis. We were all exhausted by it.

Denis also appeared by my bed and pronounced himself happy with the procedure but he made it clear that I would be kept in for a week or so to allow the site of the wound to heal properly. He would not be drawn on an exact time frame.

Another week in hospital?

Another week of managing Oisín's care and relying on friends and family? It was so frustrating. Staying in St Vincent's for the next eight days would also mean that I would miss my first baby scans. Jesus, when would I be allowed one day of a normal pregnancy? Why was everything wrapped up in such pain and worry?

All I wanted to know was that my baby was safe. I just needed to know that they had made it through three surgeries but they were still too little to give any signs. I needed proof that the baby was fine but what could I do? Yes, I was trapped in St Vincent's for the next eight days but there must be something I could organise, I thought. Then I had a eureka moment.

The wonderful Ann O'Doherty's name leapt into my mind. She had been so supportive of me at the time of my diagnosis that I decided to seek her help. That Sunday night, I asked for a notebook and a pen and scribbled a note asking her to call in to me. I slipped out of my room, went along the darkened corridors slowly and hobbled down the stairs to her Breast Check examination area where I left the note on her desk, marked for her attention.

First thing the next morning, Ann bounded into my room and asked me what she could do to help. I took a deep breath and outlined my unusual request. I needed a scan of the baby on one of her radiology machines.

No problem, she replied, and headed off. A few minutes later, she rang to say that she had arranged for the in-house radiologist to scan me early the next morning, before his usual patients. I thanked her profusely, and spent the day mulling over my new appointment. That night, I had almost the worst night's sleep since the whole ordeal had begun. I was in pain and the night nurse took pity on me: she kindly offered to make me tea and toast at midnight, but even that didn't work.

The black wolf was lying at the end of the bed and I was just stuck there, unmoving but drowning in anguish. I had read the word 'anguish' many times but I didn't fully understand its meaning until that bleak, black night. Anguish. All hope is lost. There is nothing. Nothing. You may look to a passer-by as if you are tucked up in a comfortable hospital bed but in fact you are seconds away from disappearing into a black hole. It is a mind minefield. Every thought is like taking a step across a landmine-filled landscape. It doesn't matter if you twist left or right, you're tripping over hidden devices and setting off explosions constantly. All I could think was that the world did not want me or my little family. They did not want to know about us. It was being made perfectly clear to me. I was growing more and more agitated. We're just not wanted, I kept thinking. How did it get to this? What if the baby hasn't made it? Who was I now?

Until four weeks ago, I had been living a perfectly normal life. Then my world had been shattered. The support beams that I thought had kept my life together had crumbled and crashed down around me and now I was marooned in that hospital bed. I had never felt so alone. I rubbed my hand. I had a cannula in again and it was so uncomfortable that I wanted to pull it out and fling it away. 'Cannula' is a Latin term meaning 'little reed'. It is a tube that can be inserted into the body for the removal of blood or insertion of fluid. Getting them in is tricky and extra treats should be showered on doctors and nurses who just fire them into the skin quickly and painlessly. Some doctors are amazing at inserting them but you learn to dread the nervous juniors who are clearly shaking as they approach you and you know it's going to be sore. That night everything hurt and the cannula in my hand became the focus of my anger. I felt angry, sore and broken, and began to scratch madly at it.

Lying there, I felt as if I was covered in excrement. It was that dreadful. I could even smell it. In desperation I rang my mother. It was one fifteen a.m. but I had to ring her. I sobbed down the phone to her and she sleepily but gently started murmuring all the right things. Finally, through complete exhaustion, I think, I fell into a fitful sleep, terrified at the prospect of what the morning scan might bring.

My baby, my beautiful baby. What if?

Finally, dawn broke and, as arranged, Kim arrived into my room around seven thirty to accompany me to the scan – John had an urgent meeting that morning. I was so glad to see her and told her how horrific my night had been.

'You're just worried, that's all. Everything is going to be fine,' she said, over and over again. She rang John to tell him that we were on our way down and that she would call again the minute we had news. Then she grasped the handles of my wheelchair and pushed me down to Professor Risteard O'Laoide, who, it transpired, is also a consultant radiologist at the National Maternity Hospital in Holles Street so he was clearly on extremely familiar territory. We also quickly established that we all spoke Irish so that really helped lighten the mood. After we had exchanged a few pleasantries *as Gaeilge*, he rubbed the jelly on my tummy, lifted his hand to the scanner and told me he was ready to begin.

I was trembling. Then I remember quickly reminding him that we had decided not to find out if the baby was a boy or a girl – just in case he didn't have enough to be worried about as he started the scan.

He nodded. We all took a deep breath and the room

went very, very quiet. Kim was gripping my hand tightly and my heart thumped loudly. There was only one sound we wanted to hear.

We waited and waited for what seemed an age but then suddenly, miraculously, amazingly, beautifully and loudly, I heard my baby's heartbeat for the first time and the baby was there, alive and well, and it was wonderful.

I turned to Professor O'Laoide in wonder and asked, 'Is it? Is it the baby? Is that really my baby? *An báibín. Sin mo bháibín?*' He nodded. Yes.

I started to cry. Kim was sobbing and she was holding my hand as we listened to that heartbeat and suddenly nothing mattered but that. The heartbeat filled the room and all we could do was weep. Gratitude, relief and love. Such love at that moment for this tiny person. Risteard reassured me again that the baby's heartbeat was clear and present and wished me well with the rest of my pregnancy. After we had soaked all the available tissues, Kim began to wheel me back up to my room with Professor O'Laoide's words of encouragement and support ringing in my ears. I was exhilarated. We rang John.

'The baby is fine. The baby is there – heartbeat. Everything. The baby made it,' I sobbed down the phone.

There was a minute's silence and then he said, in a choked voice, 'Brilliant! That's brilliant news. I'm so proud of you. You're amazing. I'll get there as quickly as I can. Give the baby a hug from me.'

Hooray. It was time to spread the news and tell our

family and friends that my wonder-child had somehow made it through three surgeries and a raging infection. Yes, we had news again, but this time it was fabulous news. The best. We had been holding our breath for weeks and now it was time to let go.

The visitors started streaming in to hear our news. All day long, hospital staff poked their heads into my room to ask for a look at the miracle baby. The scans were produced and pored over and Professor O'Laoide had managed to perform this miracle task without revealing whether it was a boy or a girl so that excitement was still ahead of us. Amusingly, because the scan was done on a normal hospital scanner, the images were huge. They were not the cute, wallet-sized ones that new parents are usually clutching as they stumble out of the scanning room. No, these are more like the type of hard film X-rays you would have if you had broken your leg.

The baby and I had done it. *We* had made it. There were now definitely two of us in this business.

Dear Ross,

That day when we finally met you on the scanning screen, I could have sat listening to your heartbeat all day long. Nothing mattered but that sound. You were alive and you were growing happily inside me and it changed so much for me that day. Once I heard that sound, the world's background beat started again for me and I slowly began to feel part of the human race once more.

The isolation, the loneliness, the aching terror I had felt the night before ebbed away as each tear I shed rebuilt me. I was reconfigured. Your heartbeat reignited me.

We had been through so much chaos over the previous few weeks that it had seemed impossible to me that you could still be there. How could you, with only a heartbeat to help you, survive all the drugs and trauma that I had endured?

I was exhausted by this stage, worn out and feeling

profoundly anxious a lot of the time, and I was a fully grown adult. The notion that you, a teeny tiny being, could somehow thrive in the midst of all the darkness surrounding us was incredible to me.

From the minute we knew that you were on your way, I had fallen in love with you. Oisín had been such a wonderful baby and had brought us so much joy that I knew what it was like to be a mother and I was so grateful to be given the chance to do it again with you. I am often asked how we knew that it would all turn out OK in the end but, in truth, I do not have a clear answer for that question.

Yes, Professor Crown had given us medical reassurance, but setting out on that torturous journey was the biggest leap of faith I have ever had to make. Once I was handed the news that the treatment was inevitable, I had to face up to the responsibility of the decision we were making. I spent hours mulling it over and I remember your daddy asking me once, 'Do you think you can do this?' And I had to pause. Could I do it? I do not have any super powers. I am just a normal Irish mum who gets as annoyed, irritated, tired, cross and cranky as anyone else when things are difficult. If I misplaced my keys, I could really lose it, so was I really signing up to vicious treatment and a pregnancy, and promising to do both responsibly? Me? Really? I knew me. I knew what a chancer I can be, and how I can be as lazy and selfish as any person. Would I take a bet on me carrying this off?

There are few moments as profound in life as sitting in a quiet house, just you and your thoughts, and a huge issue to resolve. You stare at the familiar walls and the pictures hanging there. You twist and turn your hands. You examine your arms and your feet, and you scratch your head and you think, This is all I've got, this is me. I am only five foot two inches tall and the world outside is so much bigger. How can I take it on? Can I really expect this little heap of me to carry me through this dreadful experience?

I will lose my hair. The treatment will hurt. The nausea could be horrendous.

And so I sat thinking it all through and as I sat there twisting and turning my hands everything became clear as, for once, I realised that it was actually not just about me any more. It was about you and giving you the best chance.

You were here.

You had done the tough part so now it was over to me. I suppose what Daddy was asking was, Did I think that, one day, I might just collapse under the strain and dissolve into a sodden mess? So I had to be fully sure that I knew what we were getting involved with and I decided to look at it in a practical way.

Rossy, I made a list of all the reasons I thought you and I might be OK. I looked around me and counted up all the supporters I had and assessed the situation as calmly and practically as I could.

Starting with Daddy: was he going to be there every step of the way? Well, seeing as he was the one guiding us steadily at that point, our North Star, I kind of knew he would be there for the duration.

Had I enough people around me to help if I needed to press the 'emergency' button at any time? I thought so.

Had I been tested before? Yes, after my dad's sad death. It had floored me for years, but somehow I had emerged from the sadness, married someone wonderful and was now setting up a family of my own.

How much did I want this new baby in my life? That one was easy. I wanted you so much that my relief that you had appeared at all stopped my heart when I thought about it.

I wanted you for myself, but I also wanted you for Daddy and, of course, for Oisín. The idea that he might gain a brother or sister out of this nightmare was a huge source of comfort for me. We love him so much, and he has brought us such happiness that we knew that if a brother or sister was going to be even a fraction as fantastic as he is, it would all be worth it. Another version of our wonderful Oisín? Definitely.

He was just seven months old at this stage and was such fun to be around that I was utterly seduced by the idea of him having someone else to share his little world. Two of you? Could I really be that lucky?

The decision to forge ahead with the twin tracks of pregnancy and treatment was, without doubt, the toughest I have ever made but somehow I have experienced so much wonder in the world that I reckoned it might just work out.

Daddy says that once I had discovered the implications of our diagnosis I made a deal with a weeks-old foetus.

He believes that you and I made a secret deal in which I promised you that I would handle all the crappy medical stuff if you would just ignore it and simply focus on growing and thriving. It sounds like a crazy deal to me but it was all we had going for us. All I had to do was keep turning up for hospital appointments, doing what the doctors told me and it might just be OK.

And now, months and months later, I can tell you, Ross, that your heartbeat that day was the first good thing that had happened to me and your dad since the whole nightmare had begun. It lifted us, brightened us, reintroduced us to the world as expectant parents rather than as a tragedy couple. It gave us hope. A fragile hope, sure, but the odds were stacked so heavily against us that a fragile shard could light up my life better than any spotlight. You were alive, I was alive, and now we had to press on. Thank you for keeping your part of the deal, Rossy.

Buckets of love,

Mama

RULES FOR HOSPITAL VISITORS

1. Do not be more than twenty minutes late. Patients are awake from six a.m. so by the time you 'actually' drop in they have been waiting eight hours for a friendly face.

2. Do not enter a patient's room and immediately start bleating about the price of hospital parking. We would love to be worried about something as trivial as that.

3. Do not enter a patient's room without chocolates. We may pretend we don't want them but we do, actually. You can have too many grapes in this life.

4. Do not sink down heavily beside the patient, smile sadly and say, 'Well, how ARE you?' with a death sigh.

5. Do arrive with at least four funny stories from the outside world that will entertain the patient and also be good recycled material for more difficult visitors later on. You are there to help pass the time so help pass it.

6. Do offer to take washing home with you. We will not ask you to do it because that is what our mother is for, but it is considerate and shows you understand and care.

7. Do not start getting a bit agitated fifty-five minutes after you arrive as you anticipate the horror of having to go into the second hour of parking. Get over it.

8. Do not arrive with massive tomes of books that you *just know* we will love. We do not need guilt at not having read *Wolf Hall* on top of trying to recuperate.

9. Do not act weirdly if a random visitor joins the group. We are not cocktail-party hosts and we do not know how Auntie Barbara is going to chat breezily with Darren, head of sales at work, but you are both grown-up so get on with it and pretend it is not awkward.

10. Finally, ignore all previous rules. Just come. We love to see you. Please, please come. It helps. Truly. Grapes and all.

Chapter 11

Haircuts and Holidays

I spent eight long days in St Vincent's that time, and although I had been allowed home for the weekend, it was upsetting to return to the hospital for the rest of the week. I had a room to myself, and my main memories are of Oisín arriving in his buggy with one member of the family, then leaving with another. It was getting ridiculous. I was dealing with a cancer diagnosis and a pregnancy and I was still on maternity leave for Oisín. I just wanted to be hanging out having picnics in the park but instead I was stuck in a hospital room and my main role was to help John set up Oisín's babysitting rota. Eventually we hired emergency nannies to help out and they were all fantastic.

Sometimes the whole thing turned into a farce though. Once I was lying in the bed, watching my sister and my mother-in-law try to collapse the buggy and I was in hysterics, laughing. It is not the most complicated piece of kit in the world, but watching the two of them struggle to close it made me laugh. And then it made me cry. That was my buggy with my baby and I should have been outside enjoying the world with him rather than outsourcing my life to everyone around me. I was growing impatient and angry now. Every time Oisín was wheeled into my room, my heart leapt with excitement. Moments later I was in tears. He was seven months old and here he was being wheeled in and out of hospital to visit his sick mom. Terrible.

At last the wound healed sufficiently for me to be allowed home. There was a problem, though. As they were worried about the original place where the drain had been inserted, I would have to go in every day to have it cleaned and dressed. This could go on for weeks, which meant that I had to build in a daily visit to St Vincent's in the weeks before my second trimester arrived and before I could start chemotherapy when the wound had to be fully healed. The clock was ticking.

At first I did not mind the prospect of getting the bandage changed daily because I was so happy leaving the hospital. My joy at the scan and the knowledge that the surgeries were behind me really lifted my spirits. I was slowly learning that I had to be more patient and to focus on my day-to-day life. John and I decided that my plan for the next few weeks was to allow the wound to heal. I would also concentrate on the pregnancy and start thinking about my chemo, which was due to start on 17 August.

I was now obviously pregnant and felt much bigger than I had at that stage with Oisín. I still had not developed morning sickness so that side of the pregnancy was very manageable but I did have mood swings. During the day, I found that if I kept busy and active the hours would fly by, but at night the darkness would begin to seep in and I would struggle. I often moved into the spare room in the middle of the night so I didn't disturb the whole house, and I would find myself reading until dawn. The one strong symptom I had had with Oisín's pregnancy had been interrupted sleep so I would tell myself, It's not the illness, it's the pregnancy. Just like the last time. You cannot force sleep. You will be fine.

As I sat up in the bed at those unbearably lonely hours of four and five o'clock in the morning, I would try not to dwell on my situation too much. Instead I would force myself to read a book and, inevitably, just as Oisín was waking up, I would start to feel sleepy and would happily have napped for hours at that point.

It was now mid-July and our family holiday to Kerry was coming up at the end of the month. It's an annual break that we share with a large group of friends and family every summer in an idyllic spot on the Ring of

Kerry. I had been going there with the gang since I was eight so I was desperately keen to go as it would be my first ever visit with my own baby. I wanted that feeling of Kerry air in my lungs and I just knew that I would feel less anxious there.

For many years, I had dreamt of a time when I would bring my own baby to Kerry to play on the beach there and finally he was going to be with me. Kells Bay was so special to me and my whole family that I was keen for Oisín to be introduced to it as early as possible as I hoped it would be a special place for him too. I was also determined to go on the holiday as I knew it would be the last we would take for some time. First, I had to strike a deal with Denis, so I asked him nervously if he thought I could go. He laughed and said of course, but there were some terms and conditions. We worked out that I was allowed to go once there was someone who would change the wound dressings. I could swim in the sea as salt water would heal it. Great. Now all I had to do was find someone to help me with the dressings who would be free to come to my rented house every single night for two weeks.

We mulled it over at home over yet another urn of tea, and my mother remembered Mary Kavanagh. A local nurse, Mary is a sister of one of our friends in the bay, Pat. I'd met her lots over the years but I was not sure that she would even remember me. Mum pulled out her phone, scrolled through her contacts and found a number. She pressed dial and moved discreetly into the sitting room where she outlined the situation to Pat. After a few minutes, she reappeared in the kitchen, smiling as she held out the phone to me. I said hello, and heard this gorgeous voice on the phone as Mary explained to me that she was really happy to help. She would do my dressings and she instructed me to start packing as she would be waiting for me to arrive so we could begin. Again, I could hardly keep the tears away. Thanks to this wonderful woman, who hardly knew me, I was going to get a holiday.

My wound and I were off on a little break. Change that. My bump, my son, my wound and I were off on our holiday. I ran upstairs to ask John to grab the suitcases from the attic.

Before we could head off, I still had one big job to do. I had long hair and John Crown had confirmed to me that it would fall out soon after my first chemo, which was booked for three weeks' time. John and I discussed the situation and decided that I should get it cut short before the holiday so that I had time to get used to the new length. This was going to be a significant moment in my life. People often asked how I felt about losing my hair, and I thought I would be fine so I made an appointment to see my regular hairdresser, Shay. I had been going to him for many years, as I had first met him through our RTÉ Radio and TV weight loss show *Operation Transformation*. He had been Gerry Ryan's hairdresser for a long time so calling into his old Zoo salon was like dropping into a friend's place for a catch-up.

The day of the appointment came, and I walked into the salon feeling fine. When he came over to me saying, 'So what are we doing today? The usual trim?' I shook my head and panic seized me. Cancer. Cancer. Cancer. I am here because of cancer. I had only been diagnosed with the bloody thing five weeks before so the word still held incredible power over me. The baby and cancer. I started gulping and desperately tried to steady my thoughts and eventually I blurted out, 'Shay, I have cancer. I'm starting chemo soon so I have to get my hair cut.'

He stopped in his tracks. Very professionally, he recovered quickly and started babbling about options. He started to cut while I wiped my eyes. 'But this is so sudden, Ev,' he said to me, and when I added the extra news about the pregnancy, even Shay, who is pretty unshockable, went a little pale. It never ends. Just as you surmount one obstacle, the infection, you have to hurtle straight ahead for the next, pre-chemo preparation.

My anxiety had turned into impatience. I just wanted to be at home with my baby instead of stuck in a salon getting a stupid haircut that I didn't want anyway. In the days building up to the hair appointment, I had spent hours poring over photos of women with short hair and had finally found a funky style in a magazine. I had cut it out and folded it into my wallet the week before so it was a little torn and worn by the time I handed it over silently to Shay. He straightened out the picture and looked closely at it. He then started brushing out my hair and double-checking the picture as he picked up the scissors. Only then, when he had memorised the picture, did he begin to cut.

Chop, chop, chop, chop. My beautiful shoulder-length hair, which Shay and I had spent hours discussing over the years, was being cut off and piling up under my chair. Andrew Dunne, who has been doing my colour brilliantly for years, wandered over to join in the conversation and I explained to him why I did not need any colour today. Usually Andrew and I have a great laugh together, and thankfully, once he had heard my story, he started messing and making me giggle with his ridiculous stories and it somehow helped get me through.

Chop, chop, chop. I had foolishly come to this appointment on my own. I had told John I would meet him afterwards outside the salon but I wanted to be in there like any normal customer and did not want extra fuss or attention. That was a mistake. I should have brought an ally as the scissors kept cutting relentlessly until I felt like I would suffocate under a pile of hair. I had tried to avoid watching my reflection in the mirror, and chatted to Andrew, when suddenly I looked up – at a stranger.

'What do you think?' Shay asked.

'It's great, lovely. Just what I wanted,' I managed to blurt out, then ran for the bathroom to grab more bloody tissues.

I had a little private sob, then dried my eyes and went back outside. Shay and Andrew gave me a massive hug, and reassured me that they had worked with several clients over the years who had been through treatment and it would all work out in the end. Yes, their hair had grown back!

I thanked them both and headed out of the door. When John saw me with my newly chopped locks he gave me a big thumbs-up and I dissolved into tears again. It is extraordinary how much my hair mattered to me. Even with all I had been through and all that I still had to deal with, I found getting my hair cut that day one of the most physically stressful experiences I had had that summer. I suppose being forced to do something drastic to your appearance is always shocking, perhaps for women in particular. We spend hours grooming ourselves and thinking about our appearance and how we fit into the world around – and then *bam*. Control is wrested from us and we're marooned in a hair salon with a puddle of our hair at our feet. Because of cancer. Purely and simply. It is yet another shocking image from this ordeal that I stored away in my file.

I also kept thinking, If I'm finding this short haircut so shocking, how the hell will I cope with baldness?

John and I grabbed a coffee, then went home to start the holiday packing. Gradually my excitement at heading to one of my favourite places in the world began to build again. My mother is from Ballybunion in Kerry so some of my happiest times have been in that gorgeous county. I feel very close to my dad there, too. We visited Kells Bay so often as a family that I associate the place with weeks of endless fun with him and the rest of the family. I think I was eight when we first went on holiday there and, apart from one student summer when I was in America, I had gone there each year ever since with the family and friends. That annual holiday is a ritual in my life so every year when I look at my brand-new diary, the first thing I do is block off two weeks in the summer for my trip to Kerry.

Finally the day for Kerry came. Oisín and I would set off with Kim and her gang and John would follow a week later. As I packed my travel cot into Kim's car I was overwhelmed with excitement. At last I could introduce my baby to this little part of the world that meant so much to me. Six hours later, as we turned the car around the final bend and the majesty of the bay was suddenly revealed to us, Oisín started to roar his head off out of tiredness and frustration at having been trapped in a car seat for so many hours. 'DARLING,' I yelled over his cries, 'this is Kells Bay, Mommy's magic place!'

WAH WAH WAH!

Instead of crying, I burst out laughing. Thirty years after my first visit I was finally there with Oisín. It should have been a magical moment but instead he was just a normal, fed-up, cranky baby who wanted to get 'ooouuuttt.'

'It's OK, baba, it's OK!' I screamed reassuringly over his yelling.

When we pulled up outside our rented holiday home, I hopped out of the car, took a deep breath as I tried to inhale the majestic scenery and then bent over trying to touch my toes, letting the blood rush to my head. I've made it this far, I thought. I've made it this far.

My sister tapped me on the head and told me to look lively and get my baby out of the seat. I smiled back at her. Life, real life, kicked back in. Come on, there's real work to be done. We laughed as we peeled sweaty, fractious children off their car seats.

We unpacked, and then discussed dinner, and so it began. The daily routine of swimming, cooking, chatting, walking, talking, wandering, pottering, more cooking. I relished it. The days in Kerry have an amazing quality: time seems to melt and dissolve. Every year it astounds me how we all manage to switch off completely after only hours of arriving in the place. Usually when I'm there I haven't a clue what time of the day it is but that year was different: I had to keep an eye on the clock because Mary visited every evening to deal with my wound.

A real bond was created during those evening sessions with Mary as we talked about everything and anything. I lay on my side with my arm pointing up as she chatted and changed my dressing. She is a wonderful nurse and, after a few days, for the first time since the infection I began to feel well again. I slowly started to feel healthy and strong, and I could not believe the difference between my pregnancy now, and with Oisín. The previous summer when I had been pregnant with him, I took life very easy and was constantly having naps. I'm sure that I talked about my pregnancy endlessly, boring everyone to death, but this year it was completely different. We didn't talk about the pregnancy much at all. We didn't really discuss the impending treatment. We just lived each day, having fabulous food and endless walks and swims. I soaked up the stunning scenery. I tried to fill my lungs with that particular air that is unique to Kerry. I was on a countdown to a chemotherapy ward and I needed to get prepared. I needed to be mentally strong to deal with it. I was like an athlete in training. I took mental images constantly of family and friends in action in that magical place. I tried to memorise the scenery. This will all help during chemo, I thought. This will be my fuel.

Between our whole group we had rented about six houses dotted around the bay so we were busy dropping in and out of each other's homes and making plans for picnics and trips to Cahersiveen. My brother Brian had flown in from Belgium, with Maria, my nephew and niece, so having that time with him was very special. As ever, Aoileann and her son, our godson Oscar, were there too along with the rest of the Farley clan. We visited my favourite café in the world – which is sadly now closed – The Lighthouse Café, perched on the side of the cliffs on

Valentia Island, and I spent hours there with the family, fortifying myself with gorgeous food and views.

It was as if we were all on a precipice and if we didn't look down it would all be fine so we made sure not to look down. No one pushed me to talk and I suppose they took their cue from me but I felt quite calm and serene about it all, just so grateful to be there and quietly excited that the new baby would be with us next year, joining the annual pilgrimage.

It would all be fine.

Chemotherapy would be fine. Wouldn't it?

I tried to push those thoughts out of my head, and ran back into the sea for another glorious swim.

Chapter 12

Newspapers and a Phone Call

We returned from Kerry two weeks later in early August. I was now hurtling towards the chemo ward and there was no avoiding it. I decided we had to stop thinking it was never going to happen. It was going to happen and we had to make plans. And then I got a strange phone call.

One Friday evening, a journalist pal of mine phoned me and cut right to the chase: 'Evelyn, I have to ask you something awful … but is it true? Have you got breast cancer?'

I stopped in my tracks. Up to this point, we had been living in a little bubble, I suppose and suddenly I shivered:

my news was 'out there' now. 'Yes,' I replied, adding, 'but it's complicated.'

There was another pause. Then she went on, 'I'm really sorry to ask you this, but is it in any way true that you are pregnant too?'

I looked across at John, who was staring at me. He motioned to me to stay quiet.

'Why are you asking me that?' I asked cautiously.

'I overheard some journalists on our paper discussing it but they were a little confused by the whole thing so I decided to warn you that they know and they are planning on writing something this weekend.'

There had been some calls before of this nature, but as I hadn't worked out what I wanted to say publicly I had ignored them. To be honest, I was sure no one would care, and if they did, sure didn't half the world know already, given how many people we had in our lives who had known since mid-June? It is a true testament to the quality of my friends, many of whom work in the media, that the story had not reached a wider circle.

'I don't want to say any more for the moment but thank you for ringing me. I really appreciate it,' I stammered, then hung up.

John already had paper and pen out, saying, 'Right, we'd better get our thoughts together and write some sort of statement.'

Kim called up to help and we spent an hour or so, with great advice from the then RTÉ Radio press officer,

Joe Hoban, drafting a release. In it we confirmed that I had been successfully treated for breast cancer and that I was pregnant. We left it at that. We chose not to give any of the treatment details and added that I would not be discussing the matter again. We had no idea what was going to happen over the next few months so I wanted as few details out in the public domain as possible. I also knew that this was a complicated situation. Some people knew that I was pregnant, others that I was being treated for breast cancer: I felt it was my responsibility to join the dots and release a clear and concise statement that would go on the record and clarify matters. So, we confirmed the diagnosis and the pregnancy. We thanked everyone in St Vincent's for their help and medical skill, and ended by recommending that anyone with any kind of concern should get in touch with their doctor. John re-drafted it one final time that evening and then it was ready to go.

Lindsey Holmes, who runs her own Public Relations firm, Lindsey Holmes Publicity, is an old friend of ours, and she agreed to release the statement through her company. She said she would send it out the next day, Saturday, around four o'clock, and that would be that.

I just nodded when John confirmed the plan with me and then I remember saying to him that I didn't think anyone would be that interested anyway. I suspected it might get a mention on the back page of one of the papers but I reckoned that that would be it.

The next day, Lindsey confirmed to us that she had released the statement and then she called later that evening to say there had been one or two calls from the papers to double-check facts but the reaction had been as quiet as we'd expected. Grand, I thought, and we headed off to bed.

The following morning, John went to the supermarket early to get some shopping and when he returned, rather than opening the door with his key, he rang the bell. I wandered down to let him in. He was standing outside with a weird expression on his face. He silently held up several newspapers.

I was on the front page of a couple of them. I nearly fainted. Of course, it was August, so there was not much news around but I suppose the headlines were tantalising for any sub-editor. There were the details of our nightmare for everyone to see in black and white. Basically the headlines could be summed up in the following words, but in different order: 'Gerry Ryan, tragic, cancer, sidekick, pregnancy, brave.' And whatever you're having yourself.

Poor Gerry. Seeing him again on the front pages was sad. 'Where have you gone?' I wanted to shout. 'I miss you. Come back.'

Once I'd got over the shock of the papers having printed the story, I was able to relax: the truth was out there now and I had nothing to hide. And in fairness the papers all wrote extremely supportive pieces about my news. On *The Gerry Ryan Show*, we had had a long-running friendship with the red tops and I was chuffed that their coverage was really quite sweet.

It was surreal reading my own story in the papers. Had it really come to this? How could these reports even be true? Who was that poor girl having to go through so much? How the hell could that be me?

It is very strange to see your family and friends ploughing through this coverage, trying to connect you, the real person they know and love, with the seemingly dramatic tragedy queen featured in print.

By coincidence Ryan Tubridy had called to the house a few days before this to check how I was getting on, so on that Sunday night I talked to his producer, my old pal Alice O'Sullivan, and asked her to tell Ryan it was OK for him to talk publicly about visiting me and how I was in good spirits, dealing with the situation as positively as I could. The next morning on-air, Ryan briefly discussed my news and wished me well before moving on to the next item.

Job done, I thought.

Then, a few days later, I got an intriguing email. A woman called Brigid, whom I had met through *The Gerry Ryan Show*, had read my story in the papers. Even though we had been extremely careful not to mention any ongoing treatment, she had figured that I would be going through chemotherapy during the pregnancy. And the reason she had worked it out? It had happened to her. She was writing to me because she had had this exact experience. The email she sent was incredible and is as clear in my mind today as it was when I first read it. She had been just months pregnant when she was diagnosed with breast cancer eight years ago and she had had the nightmare of being told that she would be treated with chemotherapy during the pregnancy. Her oncologist was also John Crown.

As I read on, my heart began to beat a little faster. She had been through it. She had been pregnant too. There was only one question I needed answered and I desperately scanned the contents of the email and then it came.

The revelation.

This lovely woman, this stranger to me, Brigid was contacting me to let me know that her baby, Jack, was now a healthy, fabulous, normal eight-year-old. The miracle had happened and could happen. I now had proof.

Brigid left her mobile number on the email and told me only to call her if I wanted to. I ran for my phone and, fingers shaking, pressed the number into the keypad. One ring. Two rings and then a voice said, 'Hello.'

I tried to speak but couldn't. I spluttered down the phone and eventually managed to stumble out the words, 'Hi, it's Evelyn from *The Gerry Ryan Show*.'

She said, in the warmest, friendliest voice, 'Ah, Evelyn, you rang. That's great. I'm delighted to hear from you,' and so we began.

She told me everything, about her trips to St Vincent's for chemo, then her endless scanning at Holles Street. Just as she reached the middle of her story, I suddenly heard a young voice in the background and she asked me to excuse her: she had to deal with something for one quick minute.

'You can have your shower now and then bed, all right?' I heard her say to him, then some boyish grumbling and muttering. Brigid came back on the line, apologising for the interruption, saying, 'Now where was I?'

'Was that him?' I asked excitedly. 'Was that Jack?'

'Oh, yes, that was him, all right. Chancer wants to stay up and watch more TV.'

I started to laugh and couldn't stop. Jack was alive and well and eight years old and he wanted to stay up late and watch television. Perfect. He was behaving like every eight-year-old should. What a magical phone call.

'Thanks, Brigid,' I said to her. 'Thank you, thank you, thank you. You will never know what this phone call means.'

'Actually, I think I do,' she said, and we said our goodbyes, promising to keep in touch, which we have continued to do.

Brigid's call that night was one of the turning points for me as I prepared to face into my chemotherapy.

I kept thinking of Jack.

It could actually all be fine, I allowed myself to think.

Chapter 13

Chemotherapy, Session 1

I woke up, eyes flickering, then remembered and my stomach clenched. I was in my familiar bedroom, lying beside John, and I should have been feeling safe. But the black wolf had returned and I saw him from the corner of my eye, snarling, saliva dripping from his jaws. Then my eyes snapped open fully and he disappeared. But he had been there. There to remind me that today was the day. Day one of chemotherapy. Here to remind me that I was waking up into a terrifying reality.

I lay there quietly as the enormity of this day settled in my mind.

Images flickered through my addled brain. The wolf

had gone but he had reminded me of a moment from one of my early visits to St Vincent's weeks before. I had been waiting for my appointment when I saw a sign on a door across from me, saying, 'Day Care Oncology', and I clearly remember getting a cold feeling in the pit of my stomach and thinking, Please please please, no, not me, not ever.

And yet here we were. Today I would cross that threshold and I would enter that room. And once I stepped in, I would leave my old life behind. Once I stepped into that room, I believed that the person who left at the end of that day would have been utterly transformed. Changed in every conceivable way.

It was early on Tuesday, 17 August. Hell Day. I slowly rose, had my shower, dressed and then crept into Oisín's room, gently stroking his face to wake him. He was just eight months old. I changed his nappy and fed him but kept him in his Babygro as I was bringing him to Mum and wanted him to feel sleepy and cosy for as long as possible. I held him tightly and headed next door. Walking up the path to her house, holding a sleepy baby wrapped tightly in his favourite blanket, remains one of the darkest memories of my life. I had a feeling of otherness. As if I was watching myself from a distance. I felt I was betraying Oisín. I had promised to be there always for him yet I was heading off for the day to start something that would take me so far away from him that I couldn't mind him by myself for much longer. My stomach kept churning.

I knocked gently on the front door, and my mum appeared instantly, full of practical help and support. She took the baby from me and quickly brought him upstairs to lie in the cute travel cot she had set up for him.

We had the usual conversation, confirming nap times and feeding times, and the whole time I was shaking. Then John appeared behind me, looking tense and pale. 'We'd better go, Ev,' he said.

'Mind my baby,' I whispered to my mum, who kissed me and rubbed my short hair affectionately.

'John is going to stay in touch with me and everything here will be fine. Oisín doesn't have a clue what is going on. It'll be OK. You just try to relax and get through the day.'

I nodded and followed John out to the car. We drove the short distance to the hospital in silence. He had packed a DVD player, books, a Kindle and an iPod to help me through the day. We had playlists with happy upbeat music, playlists with gentle, soothing sounds – everything and anything that might make the day more bearable.

We arrived at the hospital and I walked swiftly into the reception area, with John behind me, dragging my bag of electrical gear. We probably looked ridiculously overloaded but I didn't care. The next five minutes. That was all that mattered. Get through the next five minutes. So, our first job? Step into the room. That room. Cross the threshold. That was all that had to happen in the next five minutes.

I took a deep breath, knocked on the door and marched in confidently. First job done.

A nurse swooped down on us, grabbed my paperwork out of my hand and said, 'Great you're here, Evelyn. Kate's going to be looking after you today. She's really experienced and will guide you through everything.'

Marching into the room seemed to have sapped all my energy and suddenly I seemed to have lost the power of speech. I simply nodded as a friendly woman appeared in front of me, introducing herself as Kate.

'Now, let's get you set up. I've been through your paperwork and we're going to take great care of you today. Follow me into this room while we get the cannula set up.'

Ah, the dreaded cannula was back in my life. In the moments as someone prepares to insert your cannula, you can't help but stare them straight in the face and will them on to do it brilliantly. I sat down, rolling up my sleeve, and the search for a vein began. I think the tension I felt in my body had translated itself to my veins as they seemed to have shrivelled up. Kate struggled to find a suitable one.

'Let's soak it in warm water to help the vein pop,' she advised. I was brought over to a sink, where Kate ran the warm water and I plunged my unobliging arm into it. She had told John to find a comfortable chair for me and to lay my things on it, so he was off sorting that out. I stood there, powerless to do anything until that damned vein appeared, so I ran my free hand over my little bump. 'Poor baba, poor baba,' I whispered to myself. Kate returned and was happy with the vein so to her credit, in the cannula went painlessly and I was led over to my chair.

It was only at this point that I began to take in my surroundings. Contrary to my expectations, the room was not the least bit frightening. There were groups of La-Z-Boy style chairs, divided into groups of four, like a train compartment. Some chairs were blue and some were brown, and the chair you got was significant, as I was soon to learn.

John settled me into a blue chair and I sank back in it. The room was very bright, sunny and buzzy. The oncology nurses were flying around and the patients were beginning to arrive in and get sorted. You could tell the old-timers from the practised way they grabbed the blue seats: they were far superior to the brown. They stretched back properly and had a table for resting your DVD on. Note to self: blue chairs from now on.

The room itself was so packed that there was no space for visitors, so John hovered close to me on a tiny stool as Kate started setting up my drips. I wondered why they didn't have spare seats for visitors and then it dawned on me. Every seat taken by a visitor is one less available for a patient. Since I was treated, the hospital has moved buildings and now they have a fantastic ward for chemo patients, which is great.

Back to my day, though, and as the set-up took a few

minutes, I started flicking through my phone to check my messages. There was a ton of them. Gorgeous, heartwarming messages from everyone in my world wishing me the best of luck. I told John's brother Brian about the battle for the blue seats and he used to text me every chemo day with some variation on 'Don't forget, blue seats are for WINNERS,' which always cheered me up. My favourite message that first day, though, was from my pal Fiona Harrison, who wrote, 'Hey, Ev, best of luck for today! And if you meet any hot single doctors, don't be afraid to give them my number!'

I loved that message. It made me laugh.

Slowly Kate was preparing the drips beside me. She explained that while they would be giving me my chemotherapy drugs in a while, they would begin with an antihistamine to help stave off a reaction and an anti-emetic to combat sickness. She then went on to tell me that in some cases, patients react to the chemo and she told me what signs to look out for. She assured me that I would know quickly if I was reacting to it because my face would become very red and I would feel extremely hot and agitated. She said that the nurses were on the alert for these symptoms all the time, so I was not to worry: if it did happen they would deal with it quickly. I nodded. Sounded like fun.

'The antihistamine is ready,' she declared, as she attached the drip to the cannula in the back of my left hand and released the switch. I took a deep breath as the first drops began to hit my system. John clutched my other hand tightly and I smiled at him as we sat there, marooned in a sea of light in the middle of the darkest day of our lives.

The antihistamine took just a few minutes. Then it was time for the anti-emetic and, last, the chemotherapy.

Kate was efficiently swapping bags, checking and double-checking my name and details to ensure that the correct name was on my treatment allocation. She hung the chemotherapy drugs on the IV stand and said gently, 'Evelyn, we're now going to begin the chemotherapy treatment. Are you OK?'

I looked up at her and nodded mutely.

John squeezed my hand ever so tightly and then I just dropped my head down to rest on my chest, as the first drops began to wend their complicated path from the bag, through the tube and into my cannula. Into me. Into me and my baby.

It was too much. How the fuck did we get here? How was this happening?

Other mums-to-be were at yoga class, and I was hooked up to a chemotherapy drip. It was wrong and cruel. I felt like I was being kicked and slapped and beaten. I was surrounded by love and compassion but I felt so alone. So scared. My stomach was heaving with nervous tension.

I started weeping. Silent, snotty tears that I dragged up from the core of my soul. There was nothing I could say, nothing anyone could say. John and Kate were beside me, John rubbing my head, both of them trying to convey with every fibre of their being how sorry they both were that this terrible moment had finally come. Once the IV started, Kate stepped discreetly away.

Drip, drip, drip. Cold drop after relentless drop. I am killing my baby, I thought. I am selfishly doing this to survive and my baby, my beautiful baby who was so cosy in the womb this morning, is now swimming in a toxic chemotherapy-filled world. I felt like I had opened sluice gates and that my body was a sewer. What chance did my baby have? It didn't matter to me that I had had all the reassurances in the world. At that moment they faded away and I was sitting there terrified.

I could barely deal with this moment, so how could a fourteen-week-old foetus begin to cope?

Drip. Drip. I started panicking. I was breathing raspily, then my face turned red and I suddenly remembered Kate's advice. 'Kate,' I called, and she came running over to me. I was having a severe reaction to the drugs. She removed the drip, and I sat back in the chair, distressed, shaking and sweating. John could do nothing but stand by as Kate gave me more antihistamine. 'This will settle in a few minutes, I promise,' I remember her saying, and I trusted her. I had to. She was so calm, so reassuring, and she had children of her own – I had checked this much with her. I decided to follow her guidance completely. She told me to stay calm so I stayed calm. She told me to breathe in and out gently, so I breathed in and out gently. Eventually the world stopped spinning and we were ready to go once more.

The drip was set up again, attached to my cannula, and the medicine that would save my life was slowly released into my body again.

'Oh, John,' I whispered, 'I can't do this. I don't think that I can sit here and just let this happen. What kind of mother am I, allowing this shit into my body now?'

Then John delivered a little speech. One that got me through that day and many dark chemotherapy sessions afterwards. 'You have to think of this drug as life-saving. As giving you life, not taking it away,' he urged. 'This drug is helping you, saving you, giving you back your life. It's a good thing. Stop focusing on it as toxic and evil. This is giving life, not taking it away. Because of this you will see Oisín grow up and the baby will be unharmed. We know this works and the baby is perfectly safe.'

On and on he went, reassuring me over and over again that everything would be fine.

Eventually he said to me, 'I need you to get an image in your head of our two children on the beach in Kells Bay in a few years' time. They are hanging out at the picnic blanket, wearing cute body suits and arguing over biscuits and flasks. They are happy and normal and loving life, and you and I will just wink at each other, knowing how long we have waited for this scene. That picture needs to be in your mind all through this. We will get there. We just have to go through some crap in the meantime to get to that beach scene. The next five minutes. That is all you have to get through. The next five minutes.'

I nodded, as I let his words sink in. Slowly my pulse began to settle down and my heart rate went back to something approaching normal. I lay back in my blue chair and, after a while, I began to look around the room again. There was an air of quiet camaraderie, as patients and nurses chatted. You are not on your own. Lots of people are dealing with this. OK, they mightn't have a pregnancy bump but they have their own complications and they are just getting on with it. I had to just get on with it, I told myself. I started to drift off a little.

After a while a weird normality began to assert itself: utterly unexpected but entirely welcome. Bizarrely, I started to get used to the room. I began to notice other patients and started exchanging smiles with some of them. The atmosphere was friendly and warm. In between transfusions, when people were off their IV hooks for a few minutes, I saw they would get up and make tea and coffee for the others in their section. In the corner there was a Burco boiler and a constant supply of hot drinks and custard creams all through the day. Complimentary! I love those biscuits and proceeded to eat a ton of them.

One of the entertaining observations you quickly make about an oncology day room is that, in between people reeling off drug and treatment regimes to each other, they are reading glossy magazines and discussing loudly whether or not they like Cheryl Cole's new fringe. These people were normal, just like me, I began to realise.

It really hit me that morning. Cancer patients aren't a sub-species and no one is born to do chemotherapy. Everyone there had had a nightmare diagnosis, and while no one wanted to be there, now that we were, it was actually OK to want to discuss flimsy topics. Not every moment had to be absorbed in treatment-related conversations.

I relaxed a bit more and started to feel drowsy from the antihistamine. I half-heartedly watched a DVD but I was curious about my fellow inmates and nosily tuned in to other people's conversations. I heard parents worrying about being finished in time to do the school run, and others anxious about being absent from work. Everyone had worries. No one had planned to be there and everyone was struggling to work it out. I was feeling more comfortable. I made my way over to the coffee table and then it happened. A woman turned to me and said, 'You're Evelyn O'Rourke, aren't you?'

'Oh,' I said. 'Emm. Yes.'

'And you're pregnant, you poor thing.' She smiled warmly at me as she insisted on making my tea. I looked around the room.

And then I realised that, while I was busy feeling sorry for everyone else, they had been noticing my bump and were feeling even sorrier for me. Oh, Christ, I thought, am I really the worst case here? This is horrendous. You really do not want to stand out in an oncology room. And with my bump, even in there, I stood out. I shyly thanked her for the tea, had a brief chat about my progress and made my way back to my blue chair. I sank heavily into it.

Time dragged on, and my attention wandered for much of the day as I slipped in and out of drowsy moments. John reappeared around three o'clock, as planned, but because of the allergic reaction, my programme had been delayed so I did not finish until four.

Eventually I was released from the drip and my cannula removed. I rubbed my poor, punctured hand and John packed up all my stuff. I put on my coat, said thanks to the lovely receptionists and tracked down Kate to give her a hug and thank her for being so understanding. She hugged me back and told me she would see me in a few weeks.

A few weeks?

We have to go through all this again!

Let's not think about that. We fall back on our system. We just focus on the next job, getting the car out of the car park and going home to Oisín.

Hilariously, after my observation on the day of my diagnosis, you do get complimentary parking when you are undergoing chemotherapy so we sailed out of the door, waving our car-park ticket, clambered into the car and fixed our seatbelts. Then I exhaled and the tears came. I sobbed and sobbed and in between tears I kept reassuring John that I was actually fine, this was just a release. He nodded.

We turned for home and Mum was waiting in the doorway with Oisín. I grabbed him close to me and he tried to pull my hair, laughing as we made our way into the house.

'How was it?' Mum asked.

'I don't know,' I said. 'I have no idea. All I know is that I feel like I could sleep for a year, and I still like custard creams.'

The day of horror was finally over. The date that had controlled our waking thoughts for the previous few months had finally arrived. It was now nearly over and I was still standing. Wobbly and wrecked, but still standing.

One down. Five more blasts to go.

Chapter 14

Goodbye Hair, Hello Wig

The morning after my first chemo session, I woke in a blur. Even after ten hours of sleep, I was exhausted. After I had grabbed Oisín from my mum, changed him and put him to bed beside me, both of us had passed out instantly. He had had a great day with Mum, countless visitors dropping in to help entertain him, and I was wrung out in a way that I had never felt before. Everyone warns you about the tiredness with chemotherapy. When you have had a baby you think you know what tiredness is but this is very different. It saps you on every level. Taking chemotherapy drugs into your system is exhausting. The build-up to it, the treatment days and the emotional reaction when a session is finally over are overwhelming, and all I could do in response was sleep.

I had been told that in a three-week chemo cycle you were generally a bit tired the first week, exhausted the second week, then recovered in week three when you might be able to resume parts of your normal routine. But different people react in different ways.

Planning for treatment is like waiting around to be beaten up. It is bizarre. You are feeling healthy and well and yet you know from a certain date in the calendar that you will no longer be able to live life as you normally do. You have to be made sick to be made better and I found that extremely difficult to accept.

Before you can focus on resting and recovering, though, there is still one small medical job to be done and it involves a nurse coming to your house to introduce you to the Neulasta injection. You receive it a day or two after each chemotherapy session and it's a true wonder drug as it kick-starts the process by which you grow new, healthy white blood cells and helps you fight the infections that can attack your body after such a pounding from chemo. We were on red alert for the nurse's arrival and had been told that she would be with us after teatime in a marked car. Sure enough, at around six thirty, a car with a nursing sticker pulled up outside and the driver came to the door, introducing herself as Rachel. We nervously welcomed her in and she started explaining the process to us.

I had put Oisín into his buggy so we could focus on

her completely but he was restless, wanting to get out and move around. As his unhappy howls began, and as I was trying to absorb what Rachel was telling us, I grew increasingly stressed, trying to focus on her and listen to the poor baby at the same time. John was rocking the buggy to soothe him, but the cries were growing louder.

My mum was out so I gasped at John, 'Go next door to Deirdre and tell her she needs to mind the baby for fifteen minutes.' I must have sounded fierce because he headed off quickly with the buggy as I turned to the nurse with tears forming in my eyes. It was those moments that I found the toughest. Those moments when control seems out of reach and you need help there and then. You need people who can just step in and take charge. In our case, we were so lucky because we had oceans of support. Deirdre and Patrick Phelan are our fantastic neighbours on the other side from my mum and, with four children of their own, they are wonderful people to live beside. John was back in a split second so I imagine Deirdre took one look at his anxious face and happily took Oisín from him. The house was quiet and Rachel began her lecture again. She explained that a nurse administers the Neulasta the first time, but for subsequent sessions, you can do it yourself at home. Another unpleasant task for John to take on. It was a formidable injection, and although it is a wonderful medication, it always gave me wincing pain and I would alternately grip and punch the poor unfortunate cushion I was holding as John injected me.

Once the Neulasta was administered, that was it medically until my next blast just three weeks away. Finally it was time to face the inevitable baldness factor. Up until now I had done my best to ignore this part of the process, filing it away in my 'I must get around to thinking about these things' folder at the back of my mind but I could no longer dismiss it. Back at that first meeting with John Crown he had said to me, in no uncertain terms, that my hair would fall out twelve to fourteen days after my first chemo. He emphasised that this would definitely, absolutely and certainly happen, so to prepare for it. Until now I had put my fully hair-covered head in the sand and chosen to ignore it. Now that the first session was over, though, it was time to get my head around my upcoming baldness.

People had often asked me how I felt about losing my hair and I had always given the same answer, which was that I hoped I wouldn't mind too much. Getting it cut short by Shay a few weeks earlier had been traumatic, but I still had hair at that point and didn't know how I would cope when it all fell out. I hoped that I could dig deep enough to handle it, knowing that it was temporary, but lurking in my heart was the embarrassing worry that it might be the thing that finally broke my spirit. It is tough enough trying to deal with your changing body when you're pregnant, and with Oisín I had tried to enjoy the style challenge, but this would be completely different. Being pregnant and bald would not be an easy look to pull off.

John and I began to make plans for it. Our friend Eithne Hand who had experienced alopecia recommended a hairdressing salon in town that specialised in wigs and the effects of hair loss, so a few days later, ourselves and Eithne went there to make the purchase. We had decided that while we might get the wig there and have my hair cut a bit, we would leave shaving my full head to the weekend when we could do it in the privacy of my own kitchen.

The fitting went well, and was nearly fun. Eithne encouraged me to try on lots of different styles so I experimented with blonde and red wigs, hair colours I had never had, and we even took some photos. In the end though, the salon's sane advice was that you pick a wig that is closest to your own natural hairstyle. I finally picked out a brunette shiny, sophisticated bob-style wig and was pleased by how smart it looked on my head. I had found my new friend, my wig. We discussed the fact that everyone with a chemo wig usually looks like they have just stepped out of the hairdresser's as the wigs are always perfectly cut and styled. I remember thinking that many women in the oncology ward had looked far more groomed and glamorous then I had expected, and as I sat in the salon that day, trying on so many different styles, it occurred to me that, of course, they had all been wearing wigs.

Having agreed on my final choice, the hairdresser chopped off the rest of my short hair so that it was tight to my head, and we went out into the world with my wig under my arm. As we ambled along a sunny Ha'penny Bridge for a coffee, I kept staring at the bag, not quite believing that I had bought a wig. I couldn't quite believe that I was shortly going to be bald but Eithne was extremely encouraging and reassured me about my fears and worries for ages that day. That kind of support and help from friends was invaluable at moments like that. It was hard to accept that after all the hours spent with hairdressers and the discussions about styles over the years, soon there would be nothing there. Not one hair. I would actually put on this artificial lump of synthetic material and go out wearing it. This was what was going to happen. It was inevitable, as John Crown had gently warned me, and I needed to deal with it.

Despite everyone's advice though, I was still extremely nervous about handling the wig and knew that I needed to practise with it. I needed to get used to wearing it in privacy before I could confidently wear it in the outside world, so we decided that at the end of week three, before my next chemotherapy blast, we would go away with the baby to a hotel in Donegal for a few days on our own and play with it.

Chapter 15

How Twitter Kept Me Sane

It was time to pack self, husband, baby and wig off to Donegal. I was dreading it. The wig had a net on the inside that you had to pull front and back over your head to make sure the hairstyle sat straight. I tried pulling and pushing it at home in the hours before we left and just could not get to grips with it. I was convinced that I was going to spend the next six months hidden from the world with my stupid baldy head.

'It looks silly,' I moaned childishly, as I yanked it off for the hundredth time.

'It doesn't. It actually looks very smart and you look like you. No one will notice, I promise,' John responded.

'How do you know?' I asked him sulkily.

'OK, I'll make a deal with you. We have to call into the shops before we head off. I'll point out all the people who I think are wearing wigs and why, and you can see how hard it is to tell.'

We loaded up the car and headed off to Dundrum Town Centre, which was packed. We stood for a few minutes hanging over a balcony and then: 'See her.' John pointed at a woman slowly emerging on the travelator who looked like she had a very swishy expensive hairstyle. 'Definitely a wig.'

'How do you know?' I was fascinated.

'She's wearing an old tracksuit and her gardening shoes. No makeup, a bit of an aul bag hanging off her. There's no way she does that and then has perfect hair on top. Eyebrows have been drawn in so she's going through treatment and she is definitely wearing a wig, Now, be honest, would you ever think her hair was a wig?'

'Noooo,' I muttered reluctantly.

'There you go.' He was delighted with himself. Who knows? Maybe it wasn't a wig and this was that poor unfortunate woman's normal look, but it served a purpose for me. John's utter conviction and confidence carried me through and our ridiculous game got us through another five-minute chunk.

It was time to go. We hit the road and made our way up to Donegal. As soon as we were in the hotel car park, John told me to put on my wig. 'Try it now,' he advised.

'That's why we're here. Nobody knows you and you will never meet any of these people again.'

Like a grumpy teenager I hauled the wig on to my head. John adjusted it. I tweaked it. He readjusted it and said, 'Right, out you go.'

We got Oisín out of the car and trekked into Reception. My heart was beating so fast. Would the receptionist notice anything? Would she give me that second glance to check me out?

I needn't have worried. There was a wedding party booking in and she was swamped so she quickly checked us in and never checked me out. She smiled at me quickly, and not weirdly, wished us an enjoyable break, and we were done. Room card in our hand and first obstacle completed. John squeezed my hand. 'See? Not so hard.'

That afternoon while we were strolling around the beautiful lakeside walk near the hotel, John decided it was time to introduce me to Twitter. As a proper computer geek, he was always going on about some new social media thing or other, but he seemed a bit more loyal to Twitter than other things he had come across over the years. He had been on it for over a year and I had displayed no interest whatsoever. He was very persuasive, though. He was convinced that I would really enjoy it and relish the opportunity to connect with some of my favourite journalists and commentators and see what they were talking about. I was reluctant at first but decided to give it a go. Within minutes he had logged me on and suddenly I had a Twitter name and account. I slowly started scrolling through names and potential people I could follow. Suddenly a light bulb went on and I got it. I understood what it was all about.

Later that evening, *The X Factor* began its new season, and as we were hanging out eating dinner in front of it, John handed me my phone. 'Start looking at the #Xfactor comments,' he said. I did and they were hilarious. Quips, gags, bitchy comments, analysis – I was merrily scrolling through when John said, 'You should join in. Write something and tweet it.' So I did. I can't even remember what it was but I got a reaction from someone and I nearly fell off the couch. I responded and they got back to me, and the next minute I was in hysterics, laughing at some stupid but hilarious conversation about some eejits on *The X Factor*. John just laughed at me as I furiously tweeted my way through the show. And so it was that on that night my loyalty to Twitter began.

Now it is everywhere of course, but three years ago, it was a revelation to me how that feature on my phone came to mean so much to me over the following months. I know it sounds facile but it really did help to keep me sane during treatment. Little did I realise it that night, but there would be days over the coming months when I could barely lift my head off the pillow, when I didn't have the energy to talk to a friend on the phone and I was isolated from the outside world, but Twitter was always there to keep me connected. Regardless of how tired I was, I could always manage to hold my phone and use my index finger to scroll through my timeline and find out what was happening in the world. Journalists and Twitter queens would be having hilarious conversations about the most mundane things at eleven o'clock in the morning and I would be rolling around the bed in laughter. I have heard people in all kinds of situations describing the importance of developments like Facebook and Twitter to help them engage and connect more easily with the world, and my illness was proof of that for me. I could hop from breaking news stories to light-hearted nonsense at the touch of a screen and conduct highly entertaining conversations with complete strangers. Also, on Twitter it did not matter what you looked like. The people corresponding with me had no clue that they were talking to a pregnant, bald woman with a greeny-white pallor who could hardly get out of bed. They thought they were engaging with a (hopefully!) sometimes funny, smart Twitter user who was out there, responding to the cut and thrust of a busy modern world and not some patient trapped in her room. As I said, Twitter kept me sane and for those months I was so grateful for it.

When we left that hotel room a few days later, I was feeling much better and much more confident about my wig. I had worn it every time we left the room and no one had stopped to laugh at me. It was the end of week three in my cycle so my energy levels were good, and now I was completely comfortable with the wig it was time to go home and prepare for the second blast. We headed off on the Monday and my next chemotherapy dose was the following day.

First when we got home though, we had to shave my head. The time had come to confront the fact that my hair was falling out now. I noticed it particularly when I was in the shower, rinsing out my shampoo. As the suds vanished down the plughole, I would be holding clumps in my hand. Enough, I thought that morning, as I stood there again, clutching strands. Enough.

John has been shaving his own head for years now and has the full kit at home, so I marched into him and announced that we would do it that night.

Later that evening, after dinner, he turned to me and asked me if I was ready. I nodded, so he took my hand and led me into the kitchen. I sat down, and he grabbed a towel that he wrapped carefully around my shoulders. Then he went and got his electric razor set. He kissed the top of my head, hugged me tightly and whispered, 'Are you sure about this?'

I just nodded. I trusted no one else to do it for me. It had to be John and I'm so grateful that he, once again, found the courage to do it. He plugged in the razor, stroked my head one more time, then flicked it on.

BUUUZZZZZZZZZ. He started at the back of my head. There was nothing I could do. I just had to sit there. My body was slumped and my head was just hanging down. I was numb. I could feel the razor close to my skin, and the unfamiliar sensation of hair being shorn off my head was horrible. I was going to look terrible. Weird. A freak. No wig could fix this, I thought.

After a few minutes, John stopped. 'Now, take a look at this and see what you think.'

As he grabbed the mirror that was lying on the table, I closed my eyes and the knot of tension that had been forming in my stomach grew larger. I was going to cry. 'I don't think I can look,' I whispered.

'Please look, please look,' he cajoled.

'I can't. I can't bear it.'

'Please look – it's not that bad really.'

'OK, OK.' I took a deep breath and slowly opened my eyes, terrified about what I might see in the mirror, but when I saw my reflection I started to laugh.

John laughed too and the two of us giggled like school kids.

He had shaved 'J + E' into my hair.

I bent to swat him around the legs. 'You cheeky git,' I said to him. He just kissed the top of my stubbly bare head and went back to work. Zzzzz … the relentless shaving continued until finally there was a large lump of my hair on the floor at my feet and I was bald.

My mother popped in to inspect my new hairstyle. Or lack of hairstyle. 'Hmm … Not bad. You're very lucky, actually, because you have a good-shaped head.'

'What do you mean by that?' I asked her.

'Well, you know some people have unfortunate-shaped

heads. God help them, but they have bits of lumps or funny bits. You can be very grateful that you have quite a nice-shaped head so it looks fine,' she clarified.

'From your side of the family, then,' I added, smiling.

She kissed my stubbly scalp and put on the kettle. After all, it had been about nine minutes since we had had our last cup of tea. We drank tea and chatted about our day as John swept my hair up and put it in the bin. We didn't say much more about it. It was done. It was gone but it would be back and, for now, that was enough.

More tea, anyone?

Chapter 16

Chemo 2

It was the morning of my second blast so I texted everyone to remind them that it was chemo day and I needed all their help and support. I even instructed people not to send their messages too quickly as I would need them dispersed throughout the day. John packed my audio-visual equipment kit again and we headed off to St Vincent's. This time I had a different nurse but just as kind and competent as Kate had been. Again she knew my story and we began by trying to find the ever-elusive vein in my arm. It was proving tricky again so I suggested soaking it and went over to the sink and plunged my arm into the water. I was becoming a dab hand at this.

I reminded the nurse that I had had a reaction the last time to the medication so she assured me she would be on the lookout for me. The whole routine began again. This time I had been clever and had grabbed the coveted blue seat so, once the cannula was in, I lay back and waited for the drugs to start. I assured John that I was fine and that he could leave. He was only going to be up the road if anything happened so he should get some work done while I was being looked after. In any case, I thought he deserved a break from sitting around on an uncomfortable little stool trying to make small talk in front of a roomful of patients, which was not John's natural habitat. I was fine so he should go.

They set up the drips. Antihistamine first, then anti-emetic. Fine. Then the chemotherapy drugs. After a few minutes I was getting the symptoms again. My throat felt like it was closing over, I felt an intense rash forming on my chest, and my face felt like it had burst into flame. 'Help,' I warbled weakly. Within a flash the nurses were with me, removing the drip and feeding me more antihistamine to counteract the effect of the chemotherapy drug.

I was devastated. I'd been so sure it would be fine this time. I had spent hours counselling myself that I had only had a reaction before because it was my first time, but from now on it was going to be under control. The tears were sliding down my face and I felt like a complete loser sitting there. It's dreadful how quick we are to judge and blame ourselves. 'Come on now, pull yourself together,' I urged myself, but the tears would not stop.

As the nurses bustled around me one of them grabbed my hand and whispered, 'Are you OK? Can we do anything for you?' I just wanted one thing. I wanted John standing there to bring me home but that was not possible. I had to rest for a while and then they would give me the alternative drug that had worked so well the last time. Meanwhile they rang John and told him I was fine but that I had reacted badly again. If it suited for him to pop in to see me, it would be helpful. Poor John. Within minutes he was back, walking in the door of the chemotherapy ward. He told me afterwards that he had been in a meeting when they rang him and that his face had apparently turned ashen as he ran out of the room. He didn't even remember getting on his bike, he was in such a rush to get down to the hospital. Of course, by the time he came into me, I was calmer and the nurses had explained the situation to me and the plan for the rest of the day. We were going to have to start again with an alternative drug, so the whole regime would take longer than usual but it should be fine.

After a while, once he was sure I was happy, John reluctantly went back into work. As my mood picked up I began to flick through some *West Wing* episodes on DVD. I had brought a truckload of books with me but my concentration was dreadful. As my chemotherapy treatment progressed I found my concentration diminished week by week. I could barely sustain an hour-long DVD programme on that second chemo session, and by the third, a twenty-five-minute comedy programme was about all I could handle. I would start to watch or read something and my attention would wander and I would not absorb any details or the storyline. It was a real loss to me because I love to read and now, for the first time in years, I had oceans of time but could barely lift a book off the shelf.

Back in the ward, the warm atmosphere in the room began to soothe my nerves and I was feeling a little more relaxed when my sister's head popped around the door. She had texted me to see how long I would be there but I'd never expected her to venture in. Now, while John might not have been at his most comfortable perched on a rickety stool making small talk, my sister Kim was born for the job. She was my perfect chemotherapy companion and suddenly that day we got into a routine. John would set me up on a blue chair, hopefully, make sure I was happy, then go to work for a few hours. Kim would call in to me and spend the day balancing on that bloody rickety stool as we talked about everything and anything. She quickly got to know some of the other patients and whenever she was there I felt happier.

That second day dragged on endlessly and eventually I was finished around five o'clock. John had arrived and he and Kim helped me out into the warm September light. I barely made it to the car before I collapsed in an exhausted heap on the passenger seat. We dropped Kim home, then drove on in silence and just as we got close to home I felt a fluttering. My eyes flew open. I instantly knew the feeling. It was you, Ross, making sure that I knew you were fine. You were saying a quick hi before snuggling down for the night. Phew, I thought. We've both made it through this horrible, long day. And now time to sleep.

Dear Ross,

It's the night before my third chemotherapy and I feel OK. We had heard such terrible things about the treatment, but I want you to know that it is all going just fine. I panicked on the way in for the first session because I was so worried about you but, once I realised that we were there *because* we love you so much and everyone just wanted to do the best for all of us, it was OK. I am simply glad to be ticking off the sessions and grateful that somehow we are getting through it, five minutes at a time.

I have just put Oisín to bed. I stood over his cot for ages, stroking his head and thinking. This is a good thing. Sometimes I don't allow myself to think too much because it might all fall apart in my head so it's great to feel like I can pause occasionally and just think. Maybe it's because the first frightening chemotherapy sessions are over that I can do it. Also, talking to you helps me think more clearly sometimes, and tonight I am thinking about Daddy and how much love he shows us every day.

I would lie there at night and watch him as he rubbed Sudocrem into my demented scalp during those horrendous chemotherapy months, and I would think, This is love. Watching him play silly games with Oisín before scooping him up to hand over so we could go to yet another hospital appointment, it would strike me. This is love.

The four of us today, this is love.

Ross, all I can say to you is that I hope, in time, you find someone who will truly love you the way Daddy loves all of us. Then you will have found the best of what this amazing world has to offer.

Love,

Mama

Chapter 17

Blur

The next morning, the sound of the doorbell woke me up. Our new nanny, Mariana, was arriving to start work with us so this was going to be a red-letter day. Finally we had someone dedicated to looking after Oisín so I could stop living on favours and the (endless) goodwill of family and friends.

Our original plan had been that he would start in the RTÉ crèche when I returned to work after my maternity leave but, because of the diagnosis, we had had to change everything. I was advised that, with my treatment and the effect chemotherapy has on your system, I should avoid crowds or any situation where I might pick up a virus because my immune system would not cope well with it. I was told that the risk of infection that inevitably comes with every child's first few weeks in a crèche was best avoided so it would be better if Oisín was minded at home.

The boring reality of treatment is that you have no idea what you will be capable of so you have to set up your life to function without you actually being part of it. Everyone around you has to step in and live bits of it for you. It takes a lot of organisation and I was beginning to struggle with the baby on my own, so Mariana's arrival was perfectly timed. I clambered out of bed with Oisín as John welcomed Mariana in to the house.

When I got into the kitchen, she immediately made a beeline for Oisín. She beamed at him and he grinned back at her. They both laughed. This was a momentous day for me. Mariana was going to step into my shoes and look after this precious person because I would not be capable of doing it myself for the next few months. He was just nine months old, and don't ask me how, but from when I'd first met her at our interviews a few weeks before that, I'd known that Mariana was the right person for Oisín. She had all the energy, life and enthusiasm that was evaporating from me. Now that she was there, I could breathe a sigh of relief. John could get up and go to work in the morning, knowing that she would be there to scoop Oisín up and look after him, and not worry about how I would get through the day with him. I could rest as much as I needed to, and as Oisín would always be nearby, I could see him and play with him whenever my energy kicked in. While I was delighted to see her coming in the door, though, I had mixed emotions that day. On a practical level I was pleased that we had someone there to mind the baby but it was a very public acknowledgement that I couldn't cope with him because of my illness. That floored me. I was still technically on maternity leave for Oisín but now I was handing him over to a minder. The relief I felt at Mariana's arrival was tinged with sadness.

That first morning, then, we discussed Oisín's routine and John left. I slowly made my way back up the stairs with laughter and giggles from Mariana and Oisín wafting from the kitchen. I collapsed into bed. And slept.

And slept.

Mariana stayed with us for more than three years. She was an amazing part of our little family's life, and we were so lucky to find her.

She could not have come at a better time. The second round of chemotherapy drugs wiped me out. Because I had had that reaction, the medical team changed my regime so that I would be treated fortnightly instead of every three weeks. This was the only positive thing that had come from my reaction to the chemotherapy as it meant I would finish sooner than we had originally planned. But it meant also that I did not get the precious recovery week after every bout. My life for those winter months meant that I would undergo my chemotherapy day, come home, collapse for two weeks, then return for more. It was numbing.

I had been warned about nausea, warned about tiredness, warned that my immune system would be compromised, but nothing in the literature prepares you for the blank feeling that slowly creeps over you as chemotherapy progresses. It is like being unplugged. It's as if your battery runs so low that simple tasks like brushing your teeth or eating require you to rest afterwards. For me even talking on the phone was absolutely exhausting. The effort of having to engage in conversation was unbelievably demanding so I simply relied on texting and tweeting.

The nausea was manageable at the start. In fact, I tried not to take the anti-sickness tablets at first: I was reluctant, for the baby's sake, to take anything that was not crucial. By week three, the nausea was getting more persistent, but once I started taking the tablets, it became more manageable. I resented having to take those extra tablets though.

The tiredness was crippling and I presume that the pregnancy was part of that. In fairness, I was attacking my system with all kinds of drugs so any precious energy I had left had to go into growing the baby so there was very little left for me. I retired from the world and went to bed. Having been warned that my immune system was weak and that I should avoid crowds, I decided that the only responsible thing I could do was to stay close to home for the time being and not venture out far. Suddenly, my world was reduced to my bedroom, the sitting room and the hospital waiting rooms. I never wanted to be far from a bed in case I needed to lie down quickly in an emergency, which I know sounds crazy but I will give you some examples of how the tiredness was so physically affecting.

One evening, I was lying on the couch talking to my lovely mother-in-law Margaret when a wave of exhaustion hit me. I tried to focus on the conversation, which I had been enjoying, but everything just went blank and I knew I was about to collapse into sleep, so I had to cut her off rudely. 'Margaret, I have to go.'

'Oh, of course. Is everything OK?' she said quickly.

'Yeah, everything's fine, but I have to sleep now. Sorry, sorry,' I mumbled, as I hung up, closing my eyes and falling promptly asleep.

I woke up an hour later.

I remember another time we were having a family Sunday lunch in my mum's house and I was holding Oisín as I was feeding him. That wave of tiredness swept over me and I got a shock as I thought I was going to drop the baby. I just barked at my brother-in-law, Norman, who was sitting opposite me: 'Norm, take the baby, take the baby now, sorry, sorry…' I thrust Oisín into his arms and staggered out. I went home, next door, and slept for three hours straight.

Another morning Kim, who was practically a daily

visitor at this stage, arrived and ejected me from my bed so she could change the sheets. It was a gloriously sunny October morning and, grumbling about her fierceness, I made my way downstairs for tea. She emerged a few minutes later, popped the old bed linen into the wash and her phone rang. She stepped out into the sunshine to take the call, and I grabbed the opportunity to run upstairs and crawl gratefully back into bed with its fresh, clean linen. I was asleep by the time she came up to find me. At this point, I was under the care of Holles Street too, being scanned every fortnight there. While the baby somehow seemed to be thriving and I was profoundly grateful for that, my own life meanwhile had shrunk to either lying in bed or sitting in the car being driven to hospital appointments. It was dull and horrible.

I slept for hours and hours and hours.

Regularly I would wake up and my mum would be in my room organising a tray of food and I wouldn't have heard her come into the house. Perhaps one of the reasons the whole experience is so horrific is because you don't really remember anything about it. It's as if you're sleepwalking through your life. Of course you recognise everyone, and sometimes you can talk to them, occasionally you can even engage with the world, but generally you want to be left alone to exist. Breathing in and out is about all you can do some days.

The physical symptoms were difficult to deal with too. By this stage, my bald head was covered in red irritation patches from where it was rubbing on the pillow. I began to put Sudocrem on it before I went to bed, which really helped, but it was another sign of the toll the chemotherapy was taking on my body.

During my months of chemotherapy treatment, this was my bedtime routine. I would brush my teeth very gently as my gums were tender and I would try to prevent them bleeding. I would soak my hands in cold water for a few minutes to alleviate the itching that I regularly felt at my fingertips, then plaster my scalp with Sudocrem. Next, I tied a silk scarf over my head and laid another on the pillow to help with the irritation.

One night I looked at myself in the mirror and got a dreadful shock. I was clearly six months pregnant, so my bump was very prominent. Looking at my lovely bump and my bald head covered with Sudocrem reduced me to tears. I was sobbing at the sight of my own reflection. Looking at myself was making me cry. It is heart-breaking to admit that I found my own image distressing. And I can only imagine what it must have been like for John and my family to have to look at me and see the evidence of my pain all over my body.

One evening the itching on my hands was so bad that I had to ring my mum and ask her to come in and take Oisín as I couldn't hold him. In fact, I couldn't do anything except scratch and claw wildly at my hands. I remember standing at the kitchen sink, desperately plunging them into cold water to help with the itching, my head covered with Sudocrem and roaring crying while my mum held Oisín. I was apologising to her over and over and she kept saying, 'Sweetheart, no matter how hard it is for us it is absolutely worse for you. Don't say sorry to us. We are just here to help.'

'But what if it comes back?' I would howl at her and John. This was my darkest fear. This was the shadow over every minute of every day. What if the cancer returned? What if this was my fate and I was never going to be clear of it? It would come back, ravage my life and destroy me. What if it returned?

Every time I heard of someone else getting a diagnosis or, worse still, every time I heard of someone dying from cancer, the news would shatter me. Cancer makes you so selfish: you just keep pleading, 'Not me … please, not me. Please let my luck not run out yet. Please.'

But what if it comes back? Again and again I would lie on my bed begging John to help me through the abyss of darkness that I tumbled into regularly. What if something showed up on the next scan?

'Next five minutes,' John would remind me, as he stroked my sore head gently. 'Nothing is going to happen in the next five minutes. You are safe here and, anyway, it is not going to come back.'

'How do you know?' I would sob into his chest, clinging to him.

'Because I won't let it,' he would respond firmly. And he would gently stroke my sore head and sometimes that would be enough. Sometimes his conviction would let me finally close my eyes and get some precious sleep. Sometimes his love and certainty would be enough to banish the wolf from the end of the bed and send it off slavering until another day.

There were some darkly funny moments too, like when John went to the chemist with the prescription for the Neulasta injection and he had forgotten his drugs payment card, which covered my many medications. When the pharmacist asked for it, John explained that he didn't have it with him but he would pay for the Neulasta and keep the receipt to claim it back. The pharmacist smiled at him and said, 'No, I think you'll want to go home and get the card.' But John was busy, didn't want to waste time and kept insisting it would be OK, that he would pay for it with cash and take the receipt.

Eventually the pharmacist said, 'This medication costs two thousand five hundred euro.' After he'd picked himself up off the floor, John agreed that, yes, he would go home and get the card. I know we all complain about the state of the Irish health service, and having spent time on a trolley in A & E myself (that's another story!), I'm not going to say it's perfect, but at least when it comes to the vital drugs needed to combat this horrible disease, money is not always the deciding factor.

Despite all the pain and anxiety, though, there were pleasant moments with friends and family. I am extremely sociable, generally, and was keen to not let my treatment destroy this completely so I had made a ridiculous rule for myself: if anyone came to visit, unless I was actually asleep, I would get up and greet them. I knew that arriving up to the door to visit me was probably a fairly daunting prospect, so I wanted to make it as easy and welcoming as possible so that they would return another time. I quickly discovered that lunch dates worked best for me as my energy levels would be OK: if someone texted asking if they could visit, I would say yes immediately followed up with 'and can you bring lunch?'

I was shameless. Chats I could manage, but sandwiches were beyond me. During all this time, there was a trail of wonderful friends making their way in and out of the house, clutching lasagne dishes, posh lunch roll bags and pots of homemade soup. And we had some great conversations as people found talking to me allowed them to discuss their lives in a really intimate way. If you are sharing a slice of salami with a heavily pregnant bald woman in her pyjamas, it really does relax you: nothing you can do or say can be odder than the situation before you. I had some of the best conversations ever with friends while sitting at that kitchen table. Sometimes by the end of lunch I would be tired again and the kindness my friends showed me by walking me back up to my room and making sure I was comfortable before they returned to their busy lives stays with me. Old school and college friends dropped by with lunches and my friends in England, Michael Parke, Michael Cregan and

MaryMcAuliffe, were regular fixtures on the phone. Day by day, the time passed.

Every visit meant so much and I have no doubt those friendships and the companionship were a vital part of the healing process. I felt sorry for my older brother, Brian. He was in Brussels with his family at the time and I think he found it extremely difficult to be away from us all. He was constantly in touch with me and I felt his love and support down the phone line every time we talked.

By now it was late October and the chemotherapy sessions were beginning to roll into one. I was living in haze, in a blur. I was crawling along the bottom of the sea, only occasionally coming up to gulp some air when the baby kicked or I felt the autumnal sun on my face for a moment.

Ah, yes, the baby. It's time to talk about the baby.

Chapter 18

Life Goes On and On and On

Meanwhile, back in the womb, the baby was thriving. I was under the care of Professor Fionnuala McAuliffe in Holles Street and her quiet competence and confidence in managing my pregnancy were a great reassurance to John and myself. She was clearly an extremely experienced obstetrician and was in regular contact with my medical team in St Vincent's, which was wonderful as it meant she was always up to speed on my treatment. Because of the situation, she decided I should have a full scan every three weeks to ensure all was progressing well, so all through October, November and December John and I would troop into the hospital to get our scans done. All the nurses and midwives we met in Holles Street were incredibly kind but it didn't stop the whole experience being endlessly terrifying until each time they told us the baby was thriving.

Waiting was the worst aspect. I would finish a gruelling session of chemotherapy on a Tuesday and would be in Holles Street a couple of days later being scanned. Every scan knocked me for six. Endless questions would race around our minds. What if they find something? What if the placenta is affected? What if I get another reaction to the drugs?

Over and over we would mutter these questions to each other as we waited to be called. My stomach would be churning with a nauseating mixture of fear and exhaustion and I dreaded it, until one day when a midwife came to the rescue. It being a maternity hospital, it was always very warm in Holles Street and between my growing bump and my wig I used to feel as if I was burning up like a furnace as we sat there. When we went for our third scan, I was between chemo sessions three and four and I was wrung out. The heat in the waiting room threatened to overwhelm me. The queue was very long that day and the room got busier and hotter and hotter. We had been there for at least an hour and a half, and just when I thought I was going to faint, I did something I never do: I went back to the admissions desk and asked to speak to someone about the delay. In fairness, the receptionist looked as irritated by the whole situation as we were and she dealt very politely with me but she was clearly run off her feet. She looked up from her notes and asked me if I was OK.

'I'm here for a scan...' I started confidently, then suddenly faltered. I couldn't say the words. I was surrounded by all these happy, glowing pregnant women and I felt like such a freak.

I tried again. I took a deep breath and opened my mouth. 'I'm here for a scan and I'm finding the delay very hard because I – I—' I stopped talking. Tears formed in my eyes and the receptionist looked at me kindly, which, of course, made it worse.

'Because?' she prompted. I looked at her in panic. The words had evaporated. She was going to have me evicted for loitering at her desk. Then I saw that there was a pen on her desk and standing there, in the middle of that bustling hub of mothers-to-be, I took her notebook, turned it towards me and wrote: 'I am having chemotherapy and I think I am going to faint with the heat. Will it be long?' The tears were sliding down my face now and I couldn't wipe them away quickly enough as I turned the pad back to her. Her face paled as she read the note. She whispered, 'Take a seat and I will get you seen as quickly as possible, I promise.'

I nodded dumbly at her, struggling to wipe the tears discreetly, and turned to go back into the waiting room. I was hardly back two minutes when we were called and brought down to the scanning room.

The midwife, Valerie Kinsella, introduced herself to us as the senior midwife on the floor and she went on to tell us that for every scan after this we were to make sure we were booked in on a day that she was working and we would not have to wait. She would take us straight away. And then she began to rub the jelly on my tummy. Christ, what was she going to find? She smoothed the wand over my large bump – and bingo. There was the baby again. Beautifully alive and well, growing and hitting all the developmental points. For a few minutes the nightmare ceased. The baby was surviving. No! Better than that. The baby was thriving. She measured every inch of the baby and checked every muscle that she could, and everything was perfect. John and I grabbed hands and clung on to each other tightly as we watched the baby wriggle and squirm their way around my womb. And then it was time for our favourite part. The heartbeat. We loved it when she would turn on the sound and we could listen to the heartbeat. The racing heartbeat always thrilled us. The sweetest sound. Every beat told me that the baby was doing fine and not to worry.

Oh, Ross, I loved those precious moments in the scanning room in Holles Street. I could have listened to your heartbeat all day, darling.

Chapter 19

Home Life

Back at home, life was meandering along. Even during all the turmoil and chaos in our lives at that point, there were still many dull days, and sometimes I'd just stop in the middle of doing something, like the bloody washing (which never ends!), then suddenly realise that I'd been at a standstill for ages, frozen, and couldn't even remember why. Often I was thinking about the baby, of course, but there were many times when I was thinking about myself and John, how we were surviving all that was happening. How he was surviving it. We were living with a constant low level of fear and worry, but he was incredible, the way he minded us all. But how was that working?

While we have always loved one another and are best friends, we also argue and disagree as passionately as any other couple, but since that bleak day back in June, we had changed: we had not exchanged one cross word with each other. Unbelievable. When we had emerged from Denis' room with our diagnosis, something deep inside us had changed for ever: we couldn't risk arguing or fighting over flimsy things any more. Really, did it matter who put the stupid bins out? Playtime was over. There was too much at stake now.

Everything had become clearer and more sharply focused. We had Oisín and a new baby on the way in the most traumatic circumstances possible and every conversation and action since that day had been about protecting all of us through it. We were a family that had been set adrift in a terrible storm and we knew we had to cherish and mind each other. Every day was a tug of war with darkness. Rather than this pressure pulling us apart, though, we were very gentle with each other and kept checking that the other person was OK. At that time, John's pulse was more important to me than my own so the only time I worried about us was when I thought about having to deal with it alone. I got scared sometimes that it was too much for him. He was trying to protect all of us and carry on working at a busy job, so that was a heavy load to carry.

Before the diagnosis, I'd had no idea how John and I would cope with something like this. You hear terrible stories about families who struggle with the effects of this evil disease and how it can pull them apart. People are stricken by cancer and lose themselves so profoundly in it that they never really resurface. Nobody knows what will happen when they are at home on their own in the silence of their bedroom, confronted by the blackest of monsters, so how could I have known what would happen to us once cancer entered our lives?

Of course John and I had had our tough moments over the years, but the day we got our news, I knew that the situation would throw us high up in the air, toss us casually about, then smash us hard to the ground. I couldn't be sure that there would be anything but splinters and shards left of us. The whole experience had re-formed us. Nothing was solid any more. Cancer is the worst kind of villain because it robs you of everything: most particularly, time and control. It erupted into our life, arrogantly sweeping everything else aside and demanding our full attention so we had no idea how to manage its effects on us and our little world. We just tried to muddle through by taking care of each other as best we could. But there were days when it was a real struggle.

One afternoon, I was resting on the couch when I suddenly realised that the ticker-tape was back – the one with the words 'pregnant' and 'cancer' on it and it paralysed me. I wanted to run away. I looked at the pile of washing on the kitchen table and couldn't remember even how to put the clothes into the washing machine.

I stood up, lost in my own house, and wanted to walk to the front door, open it, step through and continue walking, just slip away quietly. At that moment, I wanted someone, anyone else to come along and take over my life because, standing there, I had no idea how to live it. Sure the building blocks were there but, like a toddler playing with Lego, I had no idea how to assemble them correctly. It felt like every time I tried, I put the blocks in the wrong place and the towers came tumbling down. Just go, I advised myself, just walk out of the door. No one will judge you. They will all understand, and you can figure it out another day but for now, just walk out the door and keep walking. For one moment, my fingers clenched in anticipation, but just as those feelings threatened to overwhelm me, I thought of John and his arm outstretched, shielding me, refusing to let me go.

It was so hard for him. His best friend had been forced to disappear into this dark cavern of illness where everything was focused on survival. He was always there but it was impossibly difficult for him as he could not take on any of the treatment for me. I do not know how he bore the new world he had been thrust into, but he rose to the challenge with such balls that it still knocks me sideways.

I suppose one of the things that helped was that, in the first weeks after the diagnosis, John had issued just one simple instruction. We had been married since 2005 so knew each other inside out. He told me he had decided that we could get through this as long as there was no self-pity. Of course I was allowed to react however I wanted to, and he would support me all the way, but he was not interested in listening to bouts of self-pity. That was his one rule. I signed up to it and for us it worked. I would wail and cry about being afraid and worried but I would never rant about our situation. I never felt the need because I never felt angry.

People often ask if we were furious about it and if we were bitter that we had been handed this dreadful sentence, but neither ever occurred to me. I was asked if I spent days thinking, Why me? but in truth, I used to think, Why not me?

Now, let me make it clear. I am no Pollyanna, but when you are aware of the world around you and all that others have to endure, I had to ask, 'Why not me?'

I knew that I had done nothing wrong and that we did not deserve this punishment, but I also knew that my diagnosis was as positive as it could be and that we had the potential miracle of a baby waiting to meet us at the end. We could even be considered lucky. And, trust me, I know how irritating that is to hear. I refuse to sign up to the belief that cancer can somehow be a blessing but, once you are thrust into its grip, all you can do is hope to be on its 'lucky' list by getting a manageable diagnosis. That is what you are reduced to begging for. Begging.

Once the doctors had told me that it was treatable, and had confirmed that the treatment would end one day and

I would get my old life back, I was ready to follow their lead. I was prepared to do anything for it to finish. I am extremely patient in some ways, when it really matters, and decided that obedience was the best way to go. I had been a disciplined convent school girl, with the importance of manners and unquestioning obedience drilled into me, so I tapped into those resources now. There were times in my life when this compliance hindered me, the overwhelming desire not to upset anyone and always to do the right thing, but it paid off while I had the treatment. I never missed an appointment and followed every instruction to the letter in an effort to make it end. I was prepared to endure any problems in the hope that one day, just as Ann O'Doherty had promised all those months ago, I would walk out of there and become a civilian again. Head down and get on with it. That was our recipe and it worked for us. It would end, that was all that mattered, and all we had to do was count down the days and the five-minute blocks until our lives were handed back to us. No self-pity but lots of ice cream was my solution. And chocolate.

I needed all the treats I could get because by the fourth bout of chemo the treatment was flooring me. Over the months since I finished it, I have met many astonishing women and men who told me that they worked right through their chemotherapy. They have described mornings when they would get up, shower, dress and throw on the wig in the car as they headed off to work in some attempt at having normality in their lives but that was never an option for me. I found chemotherapy crippling and it paralysed me. The combination of dealing with the growing pregnancy and the ravages of chemotherapy slaughtered me. The two weeks between sessions was gruelling and I had opted out of almost everything extra-curricular. My attention span was short and my memory was a little confused so ... eh? Um, sorry, what was I saying? Oh, yes, my attention span. Life and the endless hospital appointments just rolled on throughout those early winter months as I slowly and gratefully ticked off the chemo sessions in my diary.

Chapter 20

Chemo Ends and Oisín Turns One

Suddenly, it was 2 November, my last day of chemotherapy, and I felt extremely odd. While the whole experience had been tough, there had been some lovely times and moments too in the middle of all the chaos and maybe because of the chemo, it made those moments even sweeter. We had brought Oisín trick or treating to our neighbours for Hallowe'en and his bag had been stuffed full. He had been so excited being out late in the dark with his cousins and seeing all these big boys and girls dressed up at our door. While I had missed a few fortieth-birthday parties recently, the house was regularly busy with people dropping by for cups of tea. Visitors knew they were welcome and the kettle was regularly on the boil. However, chemo was ending and I wasn't quite sure what to do about it.

At this stage, we were old hands at the drill. My mum would bring me in to St Vincent's the day before my chemotherapy session for blood tests, then John would pack up a bag of DVDs, and I would wait impatiently to hear whether or not Kim would be free to sit with me. She always did make it, pushing all her commitments to one side and she never let me down. When I woke on the morning of the chemotherapy, I showered and dressed, kissed Oisín goodbye, and handed him over to Mariana for the day.

I would check in at the reception desk and John's brother, Brian, would text to remind me that 'blue seats are for WINNERS'. I would grab one and settle in, like a passenger heading off on a long-haul flight. I knew many of the nurses well by now and had made some pals among the patients, so the session would pass peaceably enough. This day, though, was different. It was tinged with excitement because if John Crown was happy, this would be my final day in Chemotherapy Land.

Usually, at some point during the session, the prof would appear to talk to me, and today I was exceptionally anxious to see him as I was hoping he would tell me what I wanted to hear — that my chemotherapy was finished and that he was signing me off. After a couple of hours in the chair, I spotted him making his way around the room.

Then his beady eye was on me. As he called me in for an examination, he congratulated me on my growing bump, which seemed much bigger since my last session. As this was the final check-up, I asked Kim – who was as ever perched elegantly on her teeny tiny uncomfortable stool – to join us. Sometimes I found that I could get a little overwhelmed with information and couldn't remember clearly what a doctor had said to me so I always found it useful to have someone with me to take notes. The prof had some trainee doctors with him that day, and as I made my way to the examining bed it seemed suddenly that the atmosphere in the room was very quiet and still. John Crown asked me politely to undress and as I lay back he firmly checked my neck, glands, tummy, under my arms and all around my back. As I was leaning forward for him to check my back, I caught sight of Kim's face and thought she looked sad. I glanced at the young doctors' faces and they, too, looked extremely serious. I asked the prof, 'Is there a problem here? What is going on?'

He shook his head. 'No, absolutely not. Nothing wrong here at all. It's great to see your pregnancy progressing well and it's wonderful that you feel so good. You are free to go, young lady. We'll be in touch, of course, but, for the moment, we're happy to finish your treatment with us today.'

Hooray!

The mood lifted and we talked about other things. As the conversation moved on, though, I was trying to work out what had happened. Then it hit me. I was so used to my body that it seemed perfectly normal for me to be bald, with a greeny-white chemotherapy pallor and a growing bump. To everyone else it was shocking. They found it harrowing to be confronted so intimately with what I was dealing with and their faces reminded me again of the horrible situation we were in. Their respect for my body and the physical evidence of what was happening to me had silenced them, and it silenced me too.

I paused for a minute and then I gabbled my thanks at John Crown and his team, and we made our way back into the day room. Kim grabbed my hand discreetly and squeezed it tightly for support.

During John Crown's examination my scar had been clear to see. My breast looked like a blank page. There was no nipple, just a line running across the middle. That day back in July, when Jackie, my nurse, had helped me peel off the bandages to reveal the scar, I had been devastated but I had had so much else to focus on since then that I had not really dwelt on it. That day with John Crown, though, I looked at it and wondered, Who owns that? It was still not familiar to me, and because I was pregnant it had swelled, like any other pregnant mother's would. I had no idea what it would look like after I had had the baby and my body settled down to normal. That seemed very far off that day though.

An hour later, I took a break and went to the bathroom, which was outside the oncology day room. It was engaged, so I leant against the wall waiting for it to free up. My gaze started wandering and I caught the eye of a woman sitting in the waiting area who was clearly staring at me. Then I noticed one or two others looking me up and down. They had registered the bald head and the cannula in my hand, ready for the next dose of drugs. Then they had spotted the bump and had clearly added two and two together. Those complete strangers had slowly realised that they were looking at a pregnant cancer patient and it was clearly shocking to them. Their reaction was shocking to me.

Seeing myself through other people's eyes was extremely difficult, but I immediately tried to put it into some sort of perspective. OK, I looked dreadful but they didn't know this was my final day of chemo and that a scan earlier in the week had confirmed that the baby was doing really well. The future looked bright. I decided to confuse them by smiling back warmly. They had the good grace to look embarrassed. I beamed at them again a few minutes later when I sailed past them to return to my blue seat for the last time.

The session was particularly long that day and it was nearly five o'clock by the time I finished and the room, which had been buzzing all day, was finally quiet. Some of the nurses came to wish me well and then John and Kim brought me back to the car. I was always a little unsteady after the chemotherapy sessions so I leant heavily on their arms but the tiredness could not take away from my quiet joy that chemotherapy was over. That night I went home, kissed Oisín, fell asleep, ate my dinner, then slept some more.

That was my routine for the next ten days until a morning when my mother came into my room with her usual breakfast tray. This time, though, instead of asking her to prop up my pillows, I asked her if we could go to the shops as I wanted to get Oisín's birthday present.

'You want to go shopping in the centre?' Peigí asked incredulously. 'Are you sure?' She put the tray down unsteadily on my bedside locker.

Laughing at the stunned expression on her face, I said, 'Yes. Will you bring me?'

'OK, but let's not stay too long.'

And so I showered, dressed, and headed over to buy my baby son an outfit for his first birthday on 2 December. Just like any other mother. And as I stood singing loudly in the shower, I got this exciting feeling that maybe, just maybe, life was slowly going to return to normal even if it was at an achingly slow pace. A fragile energy was being restored to me and I relished every minute of it.

The following days went well as I ventured out more and more. A week after that trip to the centre, I wanted to visit Kim's children at bedtime and read them their stories. During my treatment I had been extremely conscious of not worrying or upsetting them, so it had been easier to avoid them over the last few months, but now I really wanted to see them. That evening I pulled on my wig, got into my car and drove myself to their house. Norman answered the door and was stunned to see me. I explained my mission as my niece, Lia, appeared on the stairs. I instructed my sister to make tea as I visited my nieces and nephew in their beds. They were thrilled at this distraction and entertainment at bedtime and I loved it.

Once I had read a hundred stories, I made my way downstairs, drank tea and talked about everything and anything with Norman and Kim, then drove back home. Kim rang to check I had made it safely and she told me that Norman had been standing there shaking his head in disbelief when I had left.

'I suppose all he's known of you over the last few months was this dependent patient, who was being talked about as an invalid. Suddenly you come bounding into his house all full of fun and energy and it's just wonderful. We're both so thrilled.' I was thrilled too. It had felt fantastic and is a very special memory that I treasure. It had been so long since I had been out in the evening by myself, with my own car, and it felt wonderful and familiar.

I had begun to feel so well after the last bout of chemotherapy that I had even returned to reading and was flying through the piles of books that surrounded my bed. I had missed reading so much that it was great to be back enjoying them again.

And so it continued. Day by day, hour by hour my energy levels began returning to normal and when

Oisín's birthday came round on 2 December, I was ready to invite all the family and fill the house with O'Rourke and McMahon cousins. While John hates the pictures of me from that day, as he can't bear seeing me in the wig and still looking flushed from the chemo, I think they're great. I loved that day.

It had snowed very heavily the week before, and as we live near the foothills of the Dublin Mountains, we were quite badly affected. I was worried that no one would make it to the party but they all turned up, having trudged through the snow, and their determined efforts to make it to Oisín's party added to the specialness of the day for me. I remember John's brother Evin spending an hour in his car with Claire, his wife, and Dylan, Oisín's cousin, trying to reach us and eventually they did. At one point I opened the door and saw Kim, Norman and my nieces and nephew trekking through the snow: they had taken the Luas rather than risk driving. My brother Colm and sister-in-law Anita ploughed over with their daughter, Eden, and as my gorgeous nephew Daniel arrived and I realised that everyone had made it through the heavy snow, filling the house with presents and singing for Oisín, I remember thinking that he would be fine. He was surrounded by such love that, whatever lay ahead of us, he would be OK. I was so grateful at that moment.

Later on, as we were clearing up after the party, I felt a bubble of contentment rise inside me. Now I had finished chemotherapy, weeks of freedom stretched ahead as there was nothing else that could be done medically until I had had the baby. So, my plan was to enjoy this time as best I could. I was going to leave the house, go back out to the real world, and spend time having nice coffees and gentle walks.

Well, that was the original idea but Mother Nature had other notions. December was determined to hang on to that snow, and it played havoc with my cunning plan. Every time it began to thaw, there would be another snow shower so by Christmas we had been living with heavy snow for three weeks on and off. Every time I even looked at the door, my mum or John would warn me against going out. 'It's very icy. What if you slip and fall?' they would say, as I grumpily turned back, muttering to myself. They were right, of course, but I was really annoyed with this awful weather.

One morning, I had had enough and rang Colm, who is Mr Fix-It in our family. I begged him to come and collect me and bring me to Dundrum Town Centre, which is about a four-minute walk from my house but as the paths were covered in ice and snow I had been unable to go over for days.

'If you're ready to go in ten minutes, I'll bring you,' he agreed.

'Great,' I gasped, and flew around the house grabbing whatever Oisín and I would need for a morning's pottering. Ten minutes later, he pulled up outside my door and piled us into his work jeep and drove us around, dropping me off close to the front door. We barrelled our way into the centre and I was ridiculously excited. Having been cooped up in the house for so long, I felt like we had been dropped off in Las Vegas. The lights were so bright, and everything was shiny and new and I was really enjoying myself. I whizzed up and down the aisles in Tesco as I marvelled at the range of products. I felt like a tourist, it was so exciting. I relished the Christmas crowds, the buzz and the noise. We spent hours there that day until I was suddenly exhausted and had to ring Colm to take us home again. That was how small my world had become, that a trip to Tesco was a highlight. But the outing had served its purpose. I knew that I was slowly repairing, and that my old self was beginning to kick back in. I reckoned that, given some time, my old life, albeit with a new baby on board, would finally be on offer to me. I was determined to enjoy Christmas 2010.

Chapter 21

Christmas and a New Year

A few days later, Christmas Day rolled around and we had dinner in my brother-in-law Brian's house. It was a very special occasion as it was the first Christmas when Oisín would enjoy all the fun, as he had been barely three weeks old at this time last year. Also Brian and his soon-to-be-wife Sue had just moved into their house, down the road from us in Dundrum, so it was wonderful to be invited to celebrate their first Christmas in their new home. Also, truth be told, I was so tired from the pregnancy that I was delighted if anyone was willing to cook for me so the prospect of a gorgeous dinner added to my excitement.

The snow was still haunting us, so we cautiously crept

along the path into Brian and Sue's home where they had laid out a feast. John's parents joined us for dinner too and there was lots of fuss made of Oisín, which he adored. The pregnancy was weighing heavily on my mind at this point, so all distractions were welcome. Thankfully, my brother Brian, with Maria and their children, Zenon and Leda, were home from Brussels for the holidays, which really helped to keep me entertained.

New Year's Eve had to be confronted, of course, and memories of the previous one floated in and out of my mind all day. This time last year we had been different people. We had one baby and life was a dream. This year I was heavily pregnant, with the shortest hair in our family, facing into delivering the baby and undergoing radiotherapy. It was enough to make you want to go to bed but I did not. Instead, Brian and Maria called in and we had a family supper. John wanted to head off to bed but I made him stay up until twelve and we toasted each other with mugs of tea. 'Let's think about next New Year's Eve. Two babies and it will all be behind us.'

He just laughed and admired my enthusiasm. I was convinced, though. Let us get through this year and next New Year's Eve could be a triumph. I was thinking fireworks and dancing until dawn!

Once the holidays were over and the fuss about my chemotherapy had subsided, it was time to think about the birth and, truth be told, I was beginning to worry. Up until now I had pushed any dark thoughts about the baby firmly to the back of my mind but now I could register it all and started feeling panicky. There were times when I would be sitting quietly on the couch, and would suddenly feel swamped by everything. I would feel claustrophobic and I was longing for the pregnancy to be over so that John could be in charge of the baby for a while. The responsibility of carrying the baby safely through all the nightmarish stuff of the last six or seven months was beginning to hit me with great force and I longed for a day when I could hand the baby over to John and say, 'You are in charge, I am going out for a walk.' The worry was endless, but I had methods to manage it. Whenever I began to feel a fluttering of panic, I would urge John to talk about anything at all and distract me. He became an expert at rambling on about inane topics at the drop of a hat in his efforts to derail my mind's endless crash into panic.

It was getting hard to distract myself, though. My old adversary the wolf had returned and his shadow stalked my steps. It felt like he was always there lurking in the background, reminding me of the situation. One morning in early January I was lying in bed and I suddenly felt really scared. The old thoughts had started again, haunting me.

What if the cancer returns? What if the baby is struggling? What if this never ends and the fear is with me for ever? Jesus Christ, what have I done?

I became more and more distressed. I was shifting around the bed in despair, plucking at the quilt and the sheets, trying to settle myself, but I felt as if my mind was collapsing. It was terrifying. 'Come on, Ev,' I said to myself, 'just five minutes, get through five minutes.' But I couldn't banish the thoughts that were creeping up inside me like some toxic ivy that was clinging to me with a death grip. What if … what if … what if … what if …

I was trying everything to soothe myself and forced myself to think of John and the five-minute parcels we had discussed so often.

'Just five minutes. Get through five minutes,' I screamed at my reflection, but it didn't work. 'I can't TAKE THIS!' I shouted at the world. 'I CAN'T DO THIS!' I yelled, as I threw my pillows around the room. I was crying and gasping for air. I could feel myself growing hysterical. My body was violently shaking and I was beginning to shout at myself.

'You need to stop this right now,' I instructed myself, and grabbed my phone to call for help. As I struggled for breath, the room started spinning. I knew I could call John, of course, but he was probably in meetings and I would be asking him yet again to bolt out the door and come home to me when there was actually nothing wrong.

Then I thought of my brother Colm.

Mr Marvellous Fix-It. I rang him and checked if he was busy, and when he said he was OK, I hissed down the phone to him that I was in a bad way and urgently needed his company. 'I'm sorry to do this to you,' I said, 'but you know the way you keep saying that you'll do anything to help? Well, this is the time I need you. It's an emergency and I need you now before I throw myself out the window.'

'Give me fifteen minutes,' he replied, and I swear that it was hardly ten before he was standing by my bedside in his work suit and tie.

The relief when I saw him there was overwhelming. 'Thanks for coming,' I whispered to him as the tears cascaded down my face. I was whimpering with distress, and poor Colm's face had turned ashen, but he gamely kicked off his shoes and lay on the bed beside me as I collapsed into his arms, sobbing.

'Sssh, sssh,' he said, and we both lay there for a few minutes as I cried a bucketful of tears. When my howls eventually began to subside, he started telling lame jokes, trying to make me laugh. Then, out of nowhere, he asked, 'What's the story with Twitter anyway? How does it work?'

Wiping the tears away, I picked up my phone, opened up my timeline, and for the next hour I introduced him to the wonderful world of Twitter. By the end of it, he was an expert. I had calmed down completely, busy and distracted by explaining hash tags and profiles. Eventually he turned to me and said, 'All OK?' and I said, 'Yes,' nodding enthusiastically.

'I'm going to head,' he said gently, 'if that's OK with you?'

I nodded. Yes, it was fine. My dark cloud had evaporated. Colm clambered off the bed, kissed my still-scratchy head and yanked on his shoes. His phone rang and he winked at me as he made his way out of the room, chatting to whoever was at the other end.

I fell back against the pillows. I was exhausted but calm, and fell into a deep sleep for another few hours.

I actually had an appointment that night that I needed to prepare for. One of my regular jobs that I really found most pleasant. Once chemotherapy had ended, my energy levels had increased and I had discovered I had the time and interest to begin reading again so I had started doing some book reviews for RTÉ Radio 1's arts and entertainment programme, *Arena*. The series producer, Nuala O'Neill, was a former colleague from my *Gay Byrne Show* days, before I had moved across to *The Gerry Ryan Show*. She had asked me if I would like to do the odd book review for them on the show to keep me interested. She assured me that there would always be other reviewers lined up to cover so I was never to worry if I had committed to doing a review but did not feel up to it on the day of the broadcast. This was an extremely kind offer and utterly typical of Nuala's generosity. I loved doing the reviews as it reminded me of my old self. To my utter relief, reviewing books had nothing to do with bloody treatment. Being back in the radio centre, where I had spent so many years of my life working, was a treat. Late in the evening when it was quiet and peaceful was wonderful as it kept the place familiar for me. And it was fantastic to discuss something other than my all-consuming illness and pregnancy. The listeners had no idea that the woman robustly reviewing a book with Sean Rocks was heavily pregnant with a cap on her head to cover her baldness. I loved it. When I eventually returned to work, I was assigned to work on *Arena* as its full-time reporter which was wonderful as the team had become so familiar to me by then.

I was most grateful for anything that would help me mark time in those early January days. I even went into town for Elayne Devlin's fortieth-birthday party and decided bravely not to wear my wig as my hair was growing back. I had dinner in my friend Alice O'Sullivan's place another night, which was very pleasant, but I also felt confused. One part of me was enjoying pottering around with my friends and family so I wanted the pregnancy to continue for ever, but another part of me couldn't wait for it to be over. Either way, the decisions would be in our obstetrician's hands and so far Professor Fionnuala McAuliffe had refused to be drawn on her plans for the delivery. She kept telling me that we would wait and see and allow the pregnancy to develop. By December, the baby had been doing so well that we had pared back the scans. Her confidence that all was well really helped mine. In mid-January, we were heading into another appointment with her and I presumed that it would be a regular check-up as the baby's due date was still more than a month away. Then Fionnuala told us that she had been in communication with my radiation oncologist, Professor John Armstrong, and that he had indicated to her that he was keen to start planning the radiotherapy element of my treatment.

We obviously did not know when the baby would come. I might not go into labour until two weeks after the due date, which meant the end of February. More worryingly, if Fionnuala ended up carrying out an emergency Caesarean section during delivery at that late date, we would have to wait for that wound to heal before I could commence radiotherapy. That would add yet another few weeks to the process. Timing was crucial, she explained. John and I both nodded.

'With this in mind,' she added, 'how would you feel about proceeding with an elective section on Wednesday, the second of February?'

I nearly fell off my chair. We had been down this particular road before, of course, with Oisín, when we had been given just twenty-four hours' notice of our baby's birth, but this time it was different. It was bittersweet. I had been impatiently counting the days until the baby was due and now we had been given this option. For a few seconds I felt as if we were cheating. Then I thought how wonderful it would be for us to have control of something for the first time in this whole pregnancy. Would it not be great for us to be able to prepare for something at last with this baby?

We wandered off from Holles Street in a daze.

As we made our way home, with John's hand gently curling in mine as he walked and I waddled along beside him, we were silent, immersed in our thoughts. When we got back, John said it was my decision and that he would support me whatever I chose to do next. I decided to aim for Wednesday, 2 February. Oisín's birthday was 2 December so I liked the symmetry of it. The two siblings would be fourteen months apart. We rang Fionnuala's office and confirmed to them that, yes, we would be delighted to book in for 2 February. Then we told the family and slowly the excitement started to build. A new baby in any family is wonderful but this baby would be a small miracle.

That word 'miracle' kept being mentioned to us. Everywhere I went, people were fascinated by our story. Most days John would return home from work telling me how many people had asked after myself and the baby that day. This baby had really captured people's imagination and my sister predicted that we would have to build an extension to cope with the amount of presents they would receive. They. You see, we still did not know whether we were having a boy or a girl so our miracle baby was still 'they'.

The excitement and planning for the baby's arrival really helped me through those last days in January because I was struggling with the pregnancy. I used to get up and pace the house when the bump felt too heavy or uncomfortable. There was a constant low-level hum of worry in my mind. I had been so determined to proceed with the pregnancy but all the scans in the world couldn't really tell me what my baby would be like when they emerged from the womb. The stress was slowly eating me up. We crawled through January, that bleakest of months, and finally there was light at the end of the tunnel. I could begin to make plans for the baby and I was determined that it was all going to go perfectly for us. All my preparations were in place.

I had worked out Oisín's schedule for my time in Holles Street and I have it still. It always makes me smile. I would be going in on Wednesday morning and, all being well, we would go home the following Monday so it would require a lot of juggling but, with Mariana and my fantastic family and friends on hand to take care of Oisín, we should be able to work it out.

We had some names chosen, of course. If it was a boy, I was campaigning heavily for Ross as his first name and Pascal as his second, after my dad, and if it was a girl, we were going to call her Kim Margaret. For obvious reasons. But now it was a waiting game, and it was all in Fionnuala McAuliffe's hands. Tick tock.

Come on, 2 February. Let us meet our beautiful baby.

Chapter 22

Introducing …

It was now the end of January and we marked the thirteenth anniversary of my dad Pascal's death. It was still so difficult to believe that we had reached the thirteenth year without our beloved dad. We still felt the loss from his unexpected passing. He was by turns gentle, hilariously funny and extremely sociable, but also loved being at home surrounded by us and Mum, pottering in his garden or discussing the politics of the day. He was a truly brilliant sportsman too. The devastation of his sudden death lurked in all of us, and the knowledge that he never met any of his grandchildren (and there are ten) was heart-breaking. His anniversary is always a difficult day and I planned to spend it quietly at home, talking to Mum and getting things ready for the hospital. I thought a lot about Dad that day. He was a real softie and would have been so upset if he'd known what John and I were experiencing. Was I now grateful that he had been spared it? That at least he did not have to watch me dealing with the effects of the diagnosis? I would have done anything to have him home with us but the experience would have hurt him badly, I think. The thought also struck me that, hopefully, he would have been proud at the way we were handling it all as family, so I decided to take a moment and speak to him. It's not something I do much now, but I did it frequently in the early raw months when he had just died. This time, I asked him to come with me to the hospital and be with us during the Caesarean. I was very calm but very firm as I told him I needed him there to help me through. It soothed me a little to say the words.

Finally, the day was approaching, but what was going to happen next? What would this new baby be like? Would they have ten fingers and ten toes? Would everything be OK or would the grisly wolf have his way and deliver another horrible twist to our family's story? I was plagued with this one question: was there any way that this nightmare could have a happy ending?

I had felt more confident a few weeks ago but in those last hours counting down to the delivery, I was starting to tremble. The night before we were due to go into Holles Street, I was upstairs, checking my hospital bag for the umpteenth time and digging out some Babygros that had belonged to Oisín only a year before. Just fourteen months ago, Oisín had been born and John and I were on top of the world. John had just been appointed Head of 2fm and I was ecstatic at having our own beautiful baby at last. Then, within weeks, everything had changed and our lives were thrown into chaos by Gerry's death and the discovery of this evil cancer. The pregnancy was the only positive thing to have happened since then but it was scary now as it drew to an end. And, most importantly, what would that ending be? Whoever this baby turned out to be, we would be bringing them home to live with us and the responsibility of that was really consuming.

As I checked my wash bag again, I kept having flashbacks to dreadful moments. Hearing the diagnosis, the trauma of that day, then walking with my surgeon, Denis, in the garden as we discussed possible treatment options. Seeing the concern etched in my mum and parents-in-law's faces every time we had another baby scan. All those moments before and after surgery where I had had to force myself to stay calm as the grief I was feeling threatened to rise up and engulf me. That first chemotherapy session, the hair loss, the side effects, the panic. And then I tried to cancel that out with some great moments. Everything to do with Oisín had been wonderful, his every stage of development a triumph. I thought about the endless love that John had shown me during our ordeal, the support and understanding that my family and friends had supplied at every turn, all the texts, cards and emails during dark moments. I was urging myself to think positively and was also reminding myself that it was done now. Whatever happened next was out of our control and we would just have to roll with it. I stopped staring at some tiny vest of Oisín's and finally zipped up my hospital bag. It was Tuesday, 1 February 2011, and the baby was due tomorrow. This time tomorrow, I kept saying to myself. This time tomorrow. This time tomorrow.

Having double-checked the arrangements for Oisín's schedule I eventually made my way up the stairs and collapsed into bed. At this stage, I was no longer wearing my wig as my hair had grown back sufficiently that I looked kind of OK without it. We had named the different stages of my hair growth from Kojak to Sinead O'Connor to Halle Berry, and at that point I was a bit beyond Sinead O'Connor, but not quite in the Halle Berry department (hairwise!). Maternity hospitals are always extremely warm so I knew my wig would be too much and, for once in my life, I was choosing practicality over style. The wig was left at home.

Somehow, John and I got through that endless night. Each of us was regularly checking our phones to see what time it was until the alarm went off. We hugged each other, then clambered out of bed to get ready for this momentous day. My mum arrived in to mind Oisín as she had so often in the past twelve months, but this time it was different. This time she was waving us off with hope in her heart. A little trepidation maybe, but she was brimming with confidence that the birth would go really well. We had told only a handful of people the date as we needed to keep things calm and steady in our minds so we had decided to keep it low-key. John drove us in and we parked on Merrion Square, as close as he could get to the hospital's front door. As he was hauling my bag out of the car, it occurred to me again that we were simply re-creating the exact journey that so many thousands of other nervous parents had taken over the years. No one sails into a maternity hospital without some sort of apprehension or little worry skulking inside. Our worry was visible though: we were shaking a little as we contemplated what lay ahead. We checked in and made our way to the waiting area. I changed into the gown and sat down, squeezing John's hand tightly as we waited to be called. While we sat there, I was examined and checked by the midwives and doctors to ensure that all the paperwork was in order.

At around ten forty-five we were told that they were ready for us and we headed off to the theatre, where Fionnuala McAuliffe was waiting, scrubbed up and ready to go. We exchanged a few pleasantries and then I was wheeled in to have the epidural. I won't lie. Getting an epidural is not fun and I think I nearly finished off the poor nurse who was looking after me because I grabbed her hand so fiercely. I remember the theatre seemed busy enough with people buzzing around, and there was a paediatrician, who had introduced himself to us earlier. As the epidural began to take effect, John was ushered into the room in his scrubs. He came to my side and bent down so that our heads were touching.

We were still shaking yet I can recall us grinning madly at each other. John started to sing softly into my ear and I looked up at the clock. It was three minutes past eleven. I was churning with excitement and fear, and adrenalin was pumping through my body. The baby was coming. They were nearly here. Fionnuala started the Caesarean.

'Oh, John, oh, John,' I was murmuring. 'Oh, John, oh, John.' I kept repeating over and over as he stroked my head. Although I was numb from the epidural I could still feel the pressure of Fionnuala's hands on my stomach. Then there was some wriggling and then, as I was muttering madly, the moment came and Fionnuala exclaimed, 'It's a boy! You have a boy.'

And I, of course, burst into tears.

'A boy, a boy, a boy,' we cried out to each other. And my mind was whirring. Two boys. But is he OK? Is he OK? I needed to know.

As he was being quickly checked I tried to let the news sink in. Right, two boys, what did that mean? And my first thought was sports bags in the hall. I swear that was my immediate thought! I had grown up with two brothers and our hallway was always filled with sports bags. Boys and sports bags, I said to myself.

I was visualising an overflowing hallway when the

paediatrician appeared beside us holding our new baby boy. He looked me straight in the eye, and said the words I had been waiting for eight months to hear. The words that would define the rest of my life. The precious words that held our lives in the balance.

And then he said it. The most important sentence I have ever waited to hear.

'Evelyn, your baby is perfect.'

Then he handed me my baby.

This teeny tiny ball of wonder. Suddenly my world shifted on its axis. All the fear, the worry, the loneliness, the responsibility, the anxiety, the despair ebbed away. I felt like I was taking my first ever breaths myself. He was perfect. HE WAS PERFECT. And a boy. And, yes, that might mean washing a lot of football kit but, for now, we would live with perfect.

'He's perfect. He said he's perfect,' I sobbed to John, who was crying too. 'Look, he's perfect! We did it. We did it, he did it, we all did it,' I said to him, grinning like a fool.

Dear Ross,

I turn to you now, because this moment is the beginning of your story. Your adventures began then too, and, of course, they started with your name.

The anaesthetist asked me what name we had chosen and I looked full square at John and he answered: 'Ross. Ross Pascal McMahon.'

I grabbed his hand and whispered, 'Thank you,' and he kissed me on the forehead, just nodding at me.

'Well, that's a lovely strong boy's name,' the anaesthetist remarked, and I murmured in agreement. It was truly wonderful to be able to connect my dear dad with you, my baby son.

After all you had been through, I wanted you to have the strongest, most robust name I could think of. I wanted you to be able to take on the world and Ross McMahon sounds like a fellow who could do just that. I hope you agree.

You were six pounds two ounces and, yes, after all the

surgeries and the chemotherapy you were perfect. After all the worrying and anticipation you were finally here and you were simply perfect. Ross Pascal McMahon, you were here at last and you had presented yourself with ten little fingers and ten little toes and that was about as much as anyone could ask of you.

As I lay there watching Daddy pick you up for his first proper hug, a nurse offered to take our picture and that photo is such a precious image for us. We both looked wrecked, and you, Ross, were so red and so tiny. I remember looking at Fionnuala, who was still smiling at us, and the nurses, who were smiling too and, at that moment, the theatre seemed a magical place to me. I was so happy. For the first time since the previous June I felt I could breathe. I lay there, floating in a (slightly drug-induced) haze and I felt wonderful. Daddy, you and I were together and I couldn't wait to introduce you to Oisín. After a few more photos, a midwife came to take me to the recovery room and Daddy took you on up to our ward.

I kissed your head, Rossy, and told you I would be back with you very soon and you headed off in your daddy's arms. In Recovery I absorbed all the details about the new person in my life. Another boy. A son. A brother for Oisín, a new nephew for Daddy's and my siblings, a new grandson for our parents. You were only a few minutes old, and already you had titles and connections and you were loved. So loved. It felt like everyone in our world had been standing at the edge of the precipice with us too and now we had news. Now everyone could step back and breathe again. Our baby was here. Your name was Ross. You were perfect.

Worth waiting for.

Definitely worth fighting for.

Our baby son was finally here, and after all the stress and strain of the last nine months, I could finally kiss you and hug you and use our love for you to wash away the pain and distress we had endured waiting for this miraculous day.

I floated off to sleep for a while as I lay there in Recovery and my thoughts were filled with images and pictures of two little boys now. Brothers. Our sons. Two of them. Both perfect.

Time to rest now.

To the sky and back,

Mama

Chapter 23

Spreading the News

A short time later, when I was discharged from Recovery, I was greeted by two smiling midwives who wheeled me back up to my ward. They knew our story and their happiness at our news was truly wonderful. They confirmed that the baby was doing really well, that he had taken a bottle and was dressed in a cute Babygro, ready to be hugged. As we made our way along the ward, I spotted John and then I saw that he was cradling the baby on his lap. My heart leapt. My baby boy. I was transferred to my bed and Ross was nestled in beside me. Then the two midwives quietly stepped away and left us together. The ward was quiet, apart from our newborn's snuffly breathing, and John sat perched at the edge of the bed.

He had been talking to all the family and the excitement was incredible. As the word had begun to spread, his phone was going into orbit with the number of gorgeous messages people were sending us. The goodwill and love we felt for our new little baby boy was amazing, and having struggled through so many dark days in the past few months, it was incredibly soothing to be at the centre of good news for a change. The birth of this baby had really touched everyone and for months afterwards I continued to receive cards and emails from people I hardly knew, all of them so pleased that he had made it safely into the world.

That miraculous first day passed by in a mixture of nappy-changing, bottle-feeding and phone calls. In fact, there was only one disappointment for us that day and it can be blamed on the vomiting bug. The hospital was experiencing a winter outbreak of it at the time so had, understandably, clamped down on visitors. The only people allowed in were the baby's parents, so my sister and mother had to content themselves with pictures from our phone sent hourly.

It also meant that Oisín couldn't meet his little brother, which was hard. As I had had a Caesarean section, I was going to be kept in for five nights so Oisín's various carers made sure to bring him in to see us when it could be arranged. He was only allowed to go as far as the café so I would leave Ross with the nurses, go down and see him, then fly back up to the baby. I was on edge waiting to see the two of them together. Then it would really be true: we would see our little family together at last.

Of the many phone calls we made during those days, perhaps one of the most memorable was to Clare Glenane, my breast-care nurse in St Vincent's. She had known that we had a date for our delivery, and when I rang her she said, 'Has that baby arrived yet?'

Hearing her calm, familiar voice down the line was lovely. When I told her that, yes, indeed that baby had been born, that he was a boy and, most importantly, he was perfect, I still remember her excited reaction. She was so kind to us on the phone that day in Holles Street, reminding me of her sympathy and kindness on that horrible first day when she had had to be involved in breaking our dreadful diagnosis news. She was one of the people who had been involved with us from the start and hearing the warmth in her voice and her welcoming words for Ross was yet another significant moment for me.

Now, while I may have been disappointed about the ban on visitors in Holles Street, the care and attention we got from the nurses and midwives there was amazing. Fionnuala McAuliffe came to check on us and, once she was happy that we were both recovering well, she had a word with the ward sister who agreed that, under the circumstances, she would take Ross at night so that I could get some rest. Obviously I could not breastfeed, so we were focused on Ross taking to his bottle. Thankfully he settled into feeding really well. I look back to those quiet days in Holles Street with great affection: we were snuggled up together, getting to know each other after all the drama of the previous months. It was wonderful.

Oh, Ross. I spent hours and hours cradling my newborn son, staring at him as he slept and touching his face gently. How had he done it? Every decision for the previous months had been fraught with worry about the effect they could have on this teeny person and here he was, with all ten fingers and all ten toes. Tears would regularly spill down my face as I lay there, trying to drink in the baby before me. Our ward looked out over Merrion Square and I used to hold him up to the window and point it out to him. I would talk about the Oscar Wilde statue and tell stories about the history of the area. Still today, whenever I pass the building, I look up past the plaque on the Merrion Square side and take a look at our window and smile to myself: Ross' first home.

After five days it was finally time to bring him to his real home. How wonderful that seemed. Home with our baby. The morning I was discharged, we packed up our things, thanked all the nursing staff and went downstairs. John headed off to get the car, and I sat waiting for him in Reception with my little miracle boy tucked into his Rock-A-Tot car seat, warmly wrapped in a snow suit. I was just sitting there quietly thinking about how we just looked like every other mum and baby grouped there that morning. We did not look any different. Apart from my very severe hairstyle, we were just like everyone else. After all the planning, we were about to bring this little man home and there would be no midwives on call or doctors to help. The baby was John's and my responsibility now and we would have to work out our new lives with two small children day by day. Gulp!

John arrived back in, having parked the car outside, and I stepped out into the freezing cold day, leaving the warmth and security of Holles Street maternity hospital behind me. I felt a little shiver and then I caught myself. Everyone you love is waiting for you at home and they will all be around to help, I reminded myself. Then I pictured Oisín's face pressed up against the sitting-room window as he waited for us to come home with his new baby brother and felt a surge of excitement. It was going to be fantastic.

We drove home chatting to the baby, introducing him to the landmarks that would become so familiar to him over the coming years. When we arrived at the house, there were lots of cars parked outside and I recognised them all. We swung into our driveway and there was loud knocking. We looked up to see Mariana holding Oisín at the sitting-room window, both waving madly at us. John hopped out and took Ross' baby seat out of the car, then the front door opened and all our family spilled out on to the driveway. They hadn't seen him yet, so by this stage they were champing at the bit to get to hold him. We began to make our way into the house and Oisín was carried over to meet Ross. As he was not yet walking he had to be lifted up to see his new brother properly and after a minute he planted a squidgy kiss on his face. I looked up at John's parents, my mum, Kim, Colm and their children, and there were a lot of tears. There was a wonderful feeling of joy in the room, and after Oisín had formally introduced himself, Ross was passed along to everyone else for their welcome-home squeeze.

The kitchen was gleaming clean and there was a feast laid out on the table that would have fed an army. Everyone stood around drinking cups of tea, eating cake and admiring the new arrival. Again and again John and I went over the details of the last few days for everyone. We talked about the surgery, the fear beforehand, the ecstasy when our Ross was pronounced healthy. We were so excited to be home, and so grateful to be standing there with good news, presenting our gorgeous baby to the people who had carried the strain so generously with us in the months building up to this. I know it's an everyday occurrence, but in many ways it's surreal that you leave your house one day, heavily pregnant and responsible for a bump, and the next, no bump and the baby is a real live person and you are no longer the only carer.

As the reality of this struck me standing there in the kitchen, I relaxed a little. There were so many people around who wanted to help: we had so much support and

I would not have to feel this solo responsibility any more. I was smiling.

After a while, Ross was clearly tired and Oisín needed his nap so people started to fade discreetly away. We made our way upstairs to our bedroom. We had moved the rocking chair out of Oisín's room and back into ours for night feeds, and John sat down on it with both boys on his lap. That nearly finished me off. Seeing him as a proud dad holding his two boys close was a wonderful moment, and it was probably one of the most important for me. That was what it had all been about.

From those horrendously scary first days after the diagnosis, I had had this image in my mind of John and the two children, and it had sustained me during some awful hours. Finally it was here. I was standing in my own room, with Ross and Oisín being cradled by their dad. Click click, another precious picture for the album. We lay down on our bed, the boys between us. I felt weak with relief. I was exhausted by the emotions that had assailed me all day but I was elated too. As John and I lay there wrapped around the two of them, all I could hear was Ross' light breathing and Oisín's gentle snoring.

'OK?' John asked, smiling.

'Yup,' I responded, and he reached for my hand, holding it gently.

'You're amazing.'

'No, you're amazing.'

'No, I'm wrecked and need to sleep now and so should you.'

'Mm,' I murmured, as my eyelids grew heavy. And then I kissed my two perfect boys. Soon we were all asleep. All of us, I am sure, snoring loudly.

A while later, this beautiful, tranquil scene was rudely interrupted by a screaming baby, who shocked us all into life with the power of his lungs. Oisín got such a fright that he started bawling too. John and I stumbled out of bed to grab bottles and nappies.

'You take Ross and I'll take Ois,' John said, and so it began. We were suddenly thrust into the madness of life with two small children who were utterly reliant on us for everything. Before Ross arrived, Oisín was sleeping through the night and his life was ordered. That first day with a second baby in the house, I put on a wash with a small child under my arm while gently rocking a baby chair with my foot. It was then that I really started to learn the meaning of multi-tasking.

John and I met in the kitchen at some point when Oisín was being changed and I was gathering muslins for the feed and laughed. 'It's going to be kind of hectic around here,' I remarked, and John rolled his eyes. Then Oisín started to wail and Ross, my little man, was now on level eight of irritation because his bottle was one minute overdue and I ran off to fetch it. To be honest, we haven't stopped running since.

As a friend of mine said, the second baby is the game-changer. You think it's the first, but the second is the one that transforms your life. I think that is so true. And here we were with a one-year-old and a six-day-old, starting out on the new line-up. It was a busy, busy day. Later that evening, once John had put Oisín to bed and I had given Ross his late feed, we finally peeled ourselves off the sitting-room couch and crawled up to bed. We both fell asleep as soon as we hit the pillow. However, I felt as if my head had barely touched that pillow when I heard screaming. I was unused to this so was confused for a minute and then it hit me. It was three twenty-three a.m. We had a newborn baby, which meant – in no particular order – endless feeds, no sleep and bottles in the middle of the night. Oh, Jesus, what had we done? I felt a wave of panic.

We had forgotten what it would be like. We had been so focused on surviving over the last few months that we had barely discussed the reality of having a newborn back in our lives so quickly, and that night it hit me like a truck. There is nothing so powerful as a newborn's cry. You have to respond. As I got out of the bed and began to stumble to the crib, part of me was in total shock. I was a bit stunned to be honest. Three twenty-three a.m.?

Could we really do this again? Here we were back again in newborn land.

The microwave sterilisation kit was back down from the cupboard, the baby bottles were freshly scrubbed and lined up like soldiers ready for action and we were back in that all-consuming world. That night it was clear we were a busy family. And as Ross greedily gulped down the bottle, I thought, This is going to be crazy but it's what family life is all about and we're going to love it.

Sleepless nights, dirty nappies, sterilising bottles, it was all going to be part of our lives again. We would just have to get on with it and embrace it. Well, most of it. I was willing to embrace all of it except the lack of sleep. I used to dream in my sleep, now I dream about sleep. But as I rocked my baby in the chair that night I resolved that we would enjoy it all. Bring on the mess and the chaos and the unpredictability because that is so much of what life is about. It is about things being messy and raw, and having dreamt for so long of reaching this moment where the baby would be home safe and well with us, I resolved to take pleasure in it all. I was extremely aware that I had to enjoy it now as I was only getting to be a new mother for a few brief weeks before I returned to treatment and began the next phase of my life: mother of two and full-time patient. A few dirty nappies would be nothing compared to what was coming down the tracks.

Chapter 24

Counselling

So, there I was feeling very philosophical and in control on the night we brought our new baby home, but a few days later, I felt like a complete disaster. When Ross was eight days old, I woke up having fed him during the night and felt dreadful. I could hardly lift my head from the pillow and I just felt sad and battered by the world. I forced myself out of bed into the shower, and as the hot water cascaded down, I realised that I was crying. Tears were streaming down my face. I switched off the water and had a firm conversation with myself. Then I realised the tears had started again. I dressed while crying, and made my way down the stairs while crying, and barely made it to the kitchen chair before slumping into it in a heap. Then the tears turned to sobs and my body was heaving as it seemed that pools were gathering around my ankles. John and my mum were wrapped around me trying to comfort me and kept asking me what was wrong.

The problem was that there was nothing wrong. Except for the obvious, of course, such as a newborn baby, cancer treatment and all that: there was nothing *new* wrong. But I could not stop crying. I concluded that this must be the day my adrenalin and hormones had crashed because I'd had the baby. And I knew then that I had a rough day ahead. I sat at the table for an hour, sobbing uncontrollably. I felt disconnected from the world and, even worse, from my babies. Mum had taken Ross upstairs for a nap and John sat beside me holding my hand, telling me over and over again that I was going to be fine. But I struggled to believe him. I felt black. I could taste black. The colour black came alive to me that day. It paralysed me. I looked out the window at the sky and felt no joy at the winter sun that was bravely struggling to shine down on us.

I looked at baby Ross' gorgeous tiny vests and Babygros and felt nothing. I usually melt at the sight of a baby's bootee so this was totally out of character. Everything in my kitchen seemed distant and fragile and unreal. The work surfaces that I scrubbed so carefully with disinfectant, the piles of freshly washed clothes on the table, the bookshelves groaning with congratulations cards seemed to belong to someone else, somewhere else. My head was pounding. I just wanted it all to go away. I felt I was shrinking, and my body was knotted into a ball of tension. My mind was sore. Physically sore. As if it was a limb I had torn off. The pain was immeasurable. I could feel it throbbing. 'I don't think I can do this,' I sobbed. 'I don't think I can do any of it any more. I can't do radiotherapy AND the babies.'

John kept soothing me and reminding me that everyone said radiotherapy was a doddle compared to chemotherapy, but when I couldn't seem to agree with him, he eventually suggested that I talk to the Irish Cancer Society helpline to see if they could give me some guidance. I sat there, tears pouring down my face, as John rang the freephone number. When someone answered he handed me the phone. I was so upset, that I could hardly make myself understood but a friendly voice stayed with me as I haltingly blurted out my sorry tale. She was immediately sympathetic as I explained to her that I was sitting in my kitchen and couldn't face standing up from my chair.

'Have you been to ARC?' the helpline nurse asked.

'No, what's that?' I whimpered.

She went on to tell me that it was a drop-in cancer-patients' support centre and that the closest one was on the South Circular Road. She told me a little bit about their work and suggested that I go in and talk to them that afternoon. As I called out the address so that John could write it down, he was also nodding that it would be fine to call in today. I thanked the nurse and she kindly wished me the best of luck.

The tears had subsided. We started to make plans. The night before we had decided to bring the boys into town for our first family outing and register Ross' birth so John suggested that we stick with this plan and call into ARC along the way. Even though I was desperate for some sort of help, I was a bit worried that Ross' first trip out in the world would involve sitting in a car while his demented mother called into a group of strangers at a cancer-support centre. It would certainly be memorable, I supposed. John laughed at me and pointed out that Ross would prefer to hear that we had done that rather than leave me at home in the state I was in.

I felt a little better. We had a plan. A crazy, weird one but it was enough to get me out of that chair and stop me sobbing for a few minutes. We piled into the car and headed off to this unknown place. It is right down the far side of South Circular Road and, just as we were giving up hope of finding it, John spotted it. He pulled up outside and told me not to worry about time. I was to stay as long as was necessary. We kissed. I waved at the two babies in the back seat and headed on in.

I had no idea what to expect. I am not really a 'drop in to cancer support centres casually' person so my heart was hammering as I walked up the narrow path to the door. The building looked lovely, though, so I took a deep breath and rang the bell, hoping that the tears would stay away long enough for me to get across the threshold. I had no idea what I was going to say when the door opened but, hopefully, I would come up with something and muddle through.

Within a minute a smiley woman opened the door. She did not begin, 'What are you doing here?' or start a light interrogation, as I had expected. Instead, she just said, 'Hello, you are very welcome. I'm Deirdre. Would you like to come in?'

Now, remember, I had made no appointment with these people. They had had no contact with me and had no idea that I was going to arrive on their doorstep, and yet that was her opening line. Wonderful.

I hesitated for a minute. I hadn't expected it to be so easy and so friendly. It threw me.

'Oh, right, yes, yes, I would like to come in for a quick minute, if that's OK?'

'Yes, of course,' she said, and led the way into a gorgeous sitting-room area. The house was beautifully decorated and I began to relax as I read friendly notices and posters everywhere. Deirdre led me into the sitting room and guided me towards a comfy chair. There were little knots of people in the long room, sitting and chatting and drinking tea. Deirdre asked me if I would like some tea and I said yes and we had a quick chat about sugars and milk and things but my mind went into overdrive. What the hell are you doing here? I berated myself. Get out, you basket case.

I wanted to turn and run out of the door and apologise for the interruption but Deirdre was being so sweet about the tea that the least I owed her was to sit down and drink it.

She took the chair next to mine, and we exchanged some small talk about the house and how lovely it was. At no point did she say, 'What the hell are you doing here anyway?' After a little while, I apologised for the intrusion and hesitatingly told her that I was undergoing treatment and the place had been recommended to me by the Irish Cancer Society. I said that I had probably gone about it the wrong way, but that a lot had happened and I was having a bad day and needed to find out if there were more support services I could tap into.

Deirdre assured me that there were lots of things ARC could do to help me, so why didn't she get a short questionnaire and we could fill it in to help us clarify things?

I simply nodded.

She returned with the form and began gently to talk me through it. Once I started reciting my now well-worn sorry story I saw her stunned reaction. I started crying again and she was very nicely pretending not to be shocked, but as I explained that we had had the baby and I was now facing into radiotherapy and beginning to struggle with the enormity of it all, she leant forward and said, 'Evelyn, you have been through a terrible time. This has been a really tough experience for you. No wonder you feel a bit lost.'

'That's exactly it,' I replied. 'I feel lost. Do you think you can help?' I felt a little hope now. The tears were stopping. I gulped more tea and steadied myself. 'I think I need some counselling maybe.'

'We can help with lots of things including counselling,' she said. 'Now let's get some more details. How old is the baby now?'

'Eight days,' I answered promptly.

Deirdre nearly fell off her chair. 'You had the baby eight days ago?'

'Yes.'

'Right.'

I could see she had not had many patients casually dropping in eight days after having had a baby. She was probably struggling to find a section on the form that covered that.

'And where is the baby now?' she asked.

'Out in the car with my husband and with my other child.'

'Your eight-day-old baby is outside here now in the car,' she repeated faintly.

'Oh, yes, with my older child.' I nodded happily. 'And he, Oisín that is, is one,' I added helpfully.

'And he is out in the car too? You have a one-year-old and an eight-day-old with you now?'

'Oh, yes,' I said.

She must have thought I was still high on morphine. I started babbling: 'Their dad, as in my husband, drove us in, and when I'm done here, we're going to go on into town and register the baby. We had planned this as a nice outing for his first trip into town but when I woke up this morning I felt awful so that's why we detoured to here.'

At this point, I was beginning to feel much better and was happily tucking into the biscuits. As my confidence grew, Deirdre clearly needed a lie down but she never betrayed a moment of shock or misgiving to me. She kept smiling and plying me with biscuits, which I gobbled up greedily.

'Well, Evelyn, there are several options and services on offer here that might be able to help you. Let me talk to the office here and we'll have a think. But can I just say that you are going through an exceptionally demanding time and it is perfectly natural for you to feel overwhelmed. You're a new mum again and facing into a new chapter in your treatment, so we're delighted that you dropped in to talk to us today. That's exactly what we're here for.'

'Oh, I'm delighted too, Deirdre,' I responded, as I dunked another digestive in my tea. 'That sounds great. I'll head off soon but I might have another quick cup of tea before I go, if that's OK?'

'Of course,' responded Deirdre, who was probably thinking that it was easier to say yes to this lunatic than risk me dissolving into a puddle in her lovely sitting room. So I sat there, curled up in a cosy armchair, sipping tea and letting the atmosphere in that special place wash over me. There was a great buzz at times as people came and went for their massage treatments and group sessions and I felt quite comfortable taking it all in. After a while, I noticed a text on my phone from poor John, just checking in to see how I was getting on.

'Deirdre,' I called out. 'I'd better go. There's a bottle due for the baby.'

'Of course, Evelyn.' She started walking me to the door. 'It was lovely to meet you and thank you so much for calling in. I promise we'll be in touch with you shortly.'

We shook hands and I headed out to the car, where John was trying to soothe two impatient children. I waved goodbye to Deirdre and sat into my seat.

'Well?' he asked.

'It was good, actually. Lovely. Great tea.'

'Do you think they'll be able to help out with something?'

'Yes, actually, I think they will and it's a very special place. I felt quite comfortable there.'

'Clearly. You were in there so long,' John responded, smiling.

I thumped him on the arm. 'Cheeky!'

Deirdre was as good as her word. A few days later ARC got in touch to say that they would happily offer me counselling as soon as it suited me. They were recommending a series of six sessions with one of their team, and I should check my diary, then ring them with suggestions of times that suited. I was absolutely thrilled.

After my visit to ARC I felt much better but I thought very hard about the situation that I and the family were in. I concluded that I had done everything to take care of my physical health and now it was time to start thinking about the mental side. For months the focus had been on the physical well-being of myself and the baby and I had just coped with everything that had been thrown at me. Now it was time to reassess. I figured that it was a good time to get an MOT on my mental health. I believed my mental health was fine, but what if it wasn't? It was time to get a diagnosis and see what lay ahead of me. Mom of two and still in the middle of treatment.

In the months since the diagnosis, while I had had some dreadfully upsetting and traumatic times, somewhere at the back of my mind, I had had this unacknowledged yearning not to become totally consumed by the illness. I had quite liked the person I was before the diagnosis and I was hoping that she was still knocking around somewhere. I had been anxious that my basic personality might change because of my cancer experience, and while I knew it would change me in some ways, I didn't want to lose myself to the illness. I was hoping that a time would come when it would be behind me and I could return to familiarity and contentment with my life, but how was I going to get there?

I really didn't want to lose my confidence and trust in the world but there had been so many times when that basic contract had been violently tested in the past few months that I reckoned now was the time to get some help. I had never done counselling before but I was extremely keen to try it out. I had heard enough bright, smart people whom I admired discuss the fragility of our mental health so I knew I had to take responsibility for mine. More than that, I was conscious that I was going to be dealing with two tiny vulnerable people at home and that I needed to be able to handle the turbulence small children bring into your life calmly and responsibly. I was happy now to talk to a professional and get some sort of sense of the state of my emotional and mental health. Thankfully, with ARC, I could begin that within a few short weeks.

I pushed it all out of my mind for the time being, though, and gratefully sank back into the world of motherhood.

But when Ross was just three weeks old, I was yanked out of the nursery bubble and back into the medical world when a phone call summoned me to start radiotherapy. I was back on the treadmill.

Chapter 25

Radiotherapy

Everyone tells you that radiotherapy is a doddle.

I had heard this so often, that when I went for my initial assessment I sailed through the door to introduce myself. I had chosen to have my treatment in the Beacon Hospital at Sandyford under the care of Professor John Armstrong and I had picked it because it's only a couple of minutes from our house. I figured, with a newborn baby, it was probably wise to be as close to my treatment centre as possible. The hospital is a big, gleaming, modern, shiny building and on that first uncertain morning, it looked exactly the right place to be doing fancy futuristic-looking treatment.

So far so good. But first things first.

Eh, I know it's a doddle and all that, but what is radiotherapy?

It was explained to me that radiotherapy involves the use of high-energy rays to cure or control cancer. The beams destroy the cells, finishing off the work that chemotherapy has done. There are many ways it can be dispensed but, in my case, treatment was going to be given through external beam radiotherapy which meant that I was going to have to visit the radiotherapy centre every weekday for six weeks. The number of sessions you get changes from patient to patient, but once they had designed my programme, it was confirmed that I would receive about thirty sessions in all.

In practical terms, that meant I was tied to the Beacon every weekday for the next six weeks, but as it was so close to home, it should be manageable. I'd heard terrible stories about patients from places like Donegal having to trek up and down to Dublin for their radiotherapy treatment, so I was extremely grateful that I could be looked after so close to home. Also, while the sessions were daily, I was assured that the treatment would take just a couple of minutes so I could make plans and get on with my day afterwards.

At my initial consultation, Professor Armstrong explained that my skin would react as it would to severe sunburn. I was to use 100 per cent aloe vera products only and to take great care of my skin. He also warned me that, in some cases, patients' skin breaks down during the treatment but this would be temporary. He reminded me that, as I was being seen daily by the expert radiotherapy team, I would be monitored very closely and the team would be able to help and advise as the treatment progressed. So, apart from the daily appointments, the sunburn and the ongoing care needed for my skin, it was clearly a doddle!

After a few minutes, as the shock of the scale of the treatment sank in, I began to realise that when people said it was a 'walk in the park' what they meant was, it's a walk in the park *compared to chemotherapy*. Sure, radiotherapy does not render you speechless and dazed like chemotherapy does, but it's a serious, invasive process and, for the first few visits, it's quite weird. The other side effect I had been warned about was tiredness, but having a newborn baby can be quite tiring too so I reckoned I would manage that quite well. The rest of it was unknown territory.

A few days after I'd had that call from the Beacon team, I turned up for my initial assessment. I had been told that not only would they be measuring me up for my treatment programme but I would also be getting tattooed. To help with the accuracy of the treatment, a few small dots would be tattooed onto the skin around my breast and, yes, they were going to be real tattoos and, yes, they would be permanent.

That was a shock. A tattoo? That hadn't been part of my plan. The idea that this damned disease and treatment would leave a permanent mark on me (besides the scars) was infuriating. I had never had a tattoo before so was anxious about having it done. It just seemed typical of my luck that, rather than going wild when I was a student and getting some dodgy Chinese phrase inked on my back, I was going to end up with a tattoo composed of boring little black dots.

One night as I was fretting about the tattoos to John again, he said he would have one done too as a gesture of support.

I was stunned. 'Really?' I asked. 'You'd do that for me?'

'Yes,' he replied. 'Leave it with me and I'll do some research.'

He rang his old pal Hector Ó hEochagáin, a great man for a tattoo, and Hector advised him on the best parlour in Dublin.

So, one frosty afternoon, John and I headed in together to the tattoo parlour, and John got his first (and, to date, only) tattoo. He had decided under the circumstances to get my name done in Ogham writing on the back of his leg. It was a romantic gesture and I was very touched. As I sat there watching the pulsing ink needle going up and down his leg I realised that everything about our lives was quite bizarre so this was just another example of it.

Meanwhile, Kim had offered to chauffeur me to the Beacon for my assessment. We parked in the hospital car park, then made our way into the radiotherapy section. We introduced ourselves at Reception, where they asked me to confirm my medical details. When I was asked if I was pregnant, we both dissolved into giggles. I told the nurse that as I had a three-week-old baby at home, I was rather hoping that I was not pregnant again.

'Then again, with your record ...' Kim chimed in, and we both cracked up laughing again as the bemused nurse just stared at us.

We were guided towards the lift and brought down to the basement, where the radiotherapy zone is located. It is a sterile and blank place. First, I was fitted for a gown and told that I should bring it with me for every session. It was mine and mine alone and had been fitted so that all the skin that needed to be covered was covered, but all that needed to be treated would be visible and open to the rays that would soon be pointing at me. I was then brought into one of their treatment rooms, and asked to lie back on their super hi-tech scanning machines. They explained that I was to lie without moving as the beams of light criss-crossed the top half of my body. The information they would gather that day would be passed on to the team who would design my treatment programme.

I obligingly hopped up onto the metal surface and lay back looking up at the ceiling as the nurses made their last-minute checks. Then they stepped out and I was left alone in the white room as the machine began to rise up. The overhead lights were dimmed, and then the green beams of light started dancing across my torso. As the team had been positioning me correctly on the machine earlier, I had been advised not to move a muscle and I was told to hold onto the bar above my head to help me stay straight.

I was fine for the first few minutes. The room felt strange but interesting. Then, as my thoughts started to float away in the surreal setting, I began imagining that I was in a scene from a science-fiction movie and felt anxious. Having been warned not to move a muscle, now I wanted to cough and scratch my nose. I was sure I felt an itch on my ear but there was nothing I could do about it as my hands had to remain tightly clamped to the bar above my head. And as I lay there on the cold metallic slab, being spoken to through an intercom system, I began to shake a little bit. This was all a bit more intense than I had bargained for. It certainly didn't feel like a doddle.

When the session ended, I went back outside and chatted to the nurses, who were very sympathetic and reassured me that, within a few short visits, I would get used to the whirring of the machines and in time it would all seem normal. They also reminded me that the sessions should take just a few minutes, so while I was tied to coming every day for appointments, I should never be hanging around for long. I nodded and smiled. I just wanted to get the hell out of there and home to my babies.

What they did not know was that earlier, as I had been lying on the machine, I had spotted a set of long, thin drawers and each had a name written on it. It seemed to contain the details for each patient and I resolved to see if I, too, would own a drawer the next time I visited. Sure enough, a few days later when I next came to the Beacon, I discreetly checked and indeed, yes, there was my name written on a piece of tape and stuck to a drawer. I paused for a minute and stared at it. If my name was written on a piece of tape it meant that somewhere I was on a list of patients. The fact that there were so many other drawers in that room did not help: it reminded me that, while this was an enormous event in my life, I was just another patient on a list at the hospital. Seeing my name written so simply and plainly there confirmed to me, yet again, that, impossibly, I had had cancer and now had real estate in this cutting-edge cancer-curing place.

I felt the shiver run down my spine.

I was sick of seeing my name on those lists.

I had never wanted to own a drawer in the Beacon radiotherapy section, but there it was.

My name, Evelyn O'Rourke, on a drawer. The drawer of a cancer patient.

Just as I was beginning to wallow in a bout of misery, a nurse asked what I had thought of the music in the room. I said I remembered hearing a weird mix of show tunes and rap and the rather odd playlist had diverted me for a few minutes. The nurse smiled. It seemed that one of their colleagues had very kindly taken it on themselves to create playlists for the treatment room to distract the patients from the machines clunking around their heads. It was pumped out over the speakers in the room to 'entertain'. I smiled back and said goodbye to the staff and went home that first day feeling more swamped by the experience than I had anticipated.

When I went over the details with John, he decided that the one thing we could control was the music situation. He said I should ask if it would be OK to supply my own music, and once the nurses had said yes, he set about organising music for my iPod. He spent hours that first weekend creating playlists that would help me through the ten minutes or so that I would be stretched out on the radiotherapy machine and over the following weeks, hearing those familiar tunes really helped.

And the nurse was right: after those first few sessions, the clunking of the machines, the gowns, the sterility, the strangeness grew weirdly familiar, and I even made some treatment buddies during the weeks I trekked up there. Not quite a doddle, but certainly easier than chemotherapy, I concluded. Even the tattoos weren't that frightening in the end. There are a few tiny black dots around my breast and even I have to strain to see them now.

My mother in particular loved the brevity of radiotherapy. As a busy, efficient woman, she had worked out that, if you were clever about it, you could be in and out of the car park in less than an hour, thus avoiding the steep hospital parking rates. While she had the whole place sussed out in a few minutes, I took much longer to find my way around.

Because of the C-section I had had with Ross, I was

not insured to drive for six weeks after the surgery. At that point, it would be another three weeks before I could drive again. John had been talking to the family and they had this notion that I should always be accompanied to radiotherapy and were creating a rota. I thought this was crazy as the hospital was only a few minutes up the road but they refused to change their minds so we settled on a compromise. I would be driven to radiotherapy for the remaining three weeks that I couldn't drive myself and then we would reassess.

Those weeks were an intensely busy and exhausting time. I would be up with Ross during the night and would collapse back into bed as John did the morning feeds. He would wake me before he headed off to work and I would take over until Mariana arrived. Then I would hit the shower, and go to the Beacon with my designated driver. Depending on who that was, I would grab a quick coffee – if it was Kim I could be gone for quite a while! – then return home and resume life as mother to two babies. My mother, thankfully, would often swoop into my house in the evening and take baby Ross home with her for the night and those nights were extremely precious as it meant we got a full night's sleep.

It was amazing how, within a few days, that had become our routine. Everyone had been right about radiotherapy in that, compared to chemotherapy, it is manageable. I used to listen to other patients, as we sat in our gowns outside the radiotherapy rooms, while they discussed various symptoms. The main problem they complained about was tiredness.

TIREDNESS? I used to think as I was sitting there, having been up with Ross during the night. I don't want to sound unsympathetic but I'd crack up laughing (internally) when I heard worried wives muttering, 'Sean was really finding that he needed an extra nap in the afternoon during all this, it was so tiring.'

They had no idea, I used to think to myself.

I nearly looked forward to coming up to the hospital for treatment as it gave me a break from minding two gorgeous but demanding babies. Ha! Try my life and see how tired you are then, SEAN, I used to think darkly.

As I said before, cancer does not necessarily bring out the best in us. And we weren't out of the woods yet with young Ross. Within a week of my treatment starting he had decided it was time for us to get to know the inside of Crumlin Children's Hospital.

Chapter 26

Crumlin

It was the middle of March and Ross was five weeks old. We were muddling through the days when, one Saturday, I noticed he was not feeding well and, even for a newborn, seemed to be sleeping excessively. We logged his sleeping and eating for a few hours and started to get worried so we headed to the out-of-hours doctor service in St Vincent's Hospital. They advised us to get to Crumlin Hospital straight away. We had been in Crumlin just a few minutes when Ross was assessed and set up for scans. I was amazed at the speed of the reaction and they explained that with a baby so small they always intervened immediately.

As I sat beside Ross in the examining room, waiting for a diagnosis, I was beginning to feel panicky again. I was always worried that everything he had been through during the pregnancy might affect him, and now we were in Crumlin where he was clearly struggling. My pulse had quickened, and my heart was hammering. The one thing that kept me sane was that the doctor had been so reassuring. I had been shaking telling him Ross' medical history and he told me that he reckoned it would be fine once the baby got medical treatment quickly. I had been gulping for air by that stage and was clearly getting distressed at the sight of Ross lying there passively, struggling for breath.

'He's not going to die,' the doctor said to me gently. 'I know that's what you're thinking.'

And he was right. From the minute we realised that the situation was grave, I'd been on red alert and terrified about what the doctors might say. In Crumlin, they confirmed that while he would be absolutely fine, he was suffering from RSV, respiratory syncytial virus, which causes infection of the lungs and breathing passages. They assured us that, while it is very treatable, the baby would have to be kept in the hospital for a week. The doctors kept reassuring us that RSV was very common for the time of year and, once they could stabilise him, he would be fine, but my heart was still thumping out of my chest.

It felt like a near miss. The experience of sitting there

waiting for the results of the scan also taught me that my basic confidence had been truly dented. Just months before I had sat in a doctor's room and been told the most dreadful news out of the blue, and with that revalation, all the rules had been broken. Now anything could happen. I used to be the kind of person who had lucky escapes but on that day, 11 June 2010, my luck had run out and now I knew that awful things could happen to us.

But not today, not with my baby, I begged silently.

Eventually the doctors convinced me that Ross was going to be fine and they would transfer him to a room where they would set up treatment immediately. I exhaled. And inhaled, then slowly began to breathe a little more normally. We followed the nurse upstairs and settled Ross into his little bed. Then he was hooked up to wires and machines.

'He's going to be fine,' we whispered to each other.

Thankfully, he was. We just had to be patient and supremely organised as we now had two hospitals to visit every day.

The reality of having that tiny baby in hospital as I was trying to get to the Beacon every day would place more strain on everyone but we just had to get on with it.

Now our daily routine went like this: John slept at night on a tiny thin mattress at Ross' hospital bedside, and in the morning I would wait for Mariana to arrive to mind Oisín, then go to the Beacon. I would get my zap of radiotherapy for the day and then my designated driver would bring me to Crumlin, where I would take over from John. He would dash home for a few hours' sleep and go to work in the afternoons. I would spend the day with Ross in the hospital and in the evening John would return to relieve me and someone would bring me home. It sounds crazy and now I wonder how we crawled through that week, but we somehow managed to be with our sick little Ross at all times.

In some ways, I nearly enjoyed those quiet hours with Ross in Crumlin. Home was so busy, with people coming and going all the time, so once we knew he was recovering, I liked sitting there quietly with him wrapped up on my chest as I flicked around daytime television.

The worst day in this sorry saga was yet to come, though. That was the day when the radiotherapy machine broke down. It could be a contender for a top-five place of misery moments during that traumatic year.

I had gone along to the Beacon for my daily treatment as usual, and as I was lying on the metallic monster, with the loud banging noises and swooshing sci-fi lights delivering the treatment, suddenly everything stopped. A nurse came in and told me that the machine had broken down and that they would try to get it fixed and continue with my treatment later in the day, if that suited. They knew that patients counted down each session to their final one and missing one was very upsetting. More importantly, though, it was crucial that, once the regime had started, the treatment was administered regularly.

So I left the Beacon after my half-finished session and met up with my father-in-law, Brian, who drove me to Crumlin where I took over from a weary John. A few hours later, my mother-in-law, Margaret, appeared to bring me back to the Beacon, where I finished my interrupted treatment session, and then she brought me on home again.

That evening, as I lay on that loud, thunk-thunk machine for the second time that day, listening to the random songs that were playing on the speakers, I remember asking myself, Is this the worst day? Will it really ever be this crazily bad again?

I just remember leaving the hospital with Margaret, crawling home to bed and crying myself to sleep. This was getting impossible, I thought.

The next morning, however, there was news.

John rang to say that Ross had had a wonderful night and that he was off the oxygen nebuliser. Relief. Luckily, he recovered really well from there on, and a few days later he was discharged. We returned to normality. Well, our version of it.

Once we were safely home, having only to deal with one hospital in the mornings did make life seem quiet and ordered and so we ploughed on with our lives. And as I ticked the radiotherapy sessions off on the calendar, I could see that civilian life was finally beckoning. Only two weeks to go. Only one week to go. Everyone was fixated on the countdown. The day it would all be over.

My counselling at ARC had begun during this time,

and I found it was really helping. At our first session, the counsellor asked what I wanted from our meetings and I told her I wanted honesty. I believed that, other than the odd wobble, I was handling all the stresses and strains of our situation quite well, but I was worried in case I was fooling myself. I confessed to her that my dread was that one day I would be driving along the M50 or pushing a trolley down aisle thirteen of chilled foods in the supermarket and the enormity of what had happened would suddenly strike me and I would collapse. I was afraid that I would be found sobbing uncontrollably into a bag of frozen peas, and that I would have to be sedated as my life crumbled around me. I was terrified that somewhere deep, lying dormant inside me, there was a wave of anxiety that would explode some day and sweep me away. I told her I was always keen to put a brave face on things and that I hated worrying people so I needed someone like her, a complete stranger, to assess me honestly and tell me that, psychologically, I was ready for the demands of life post-treatment.

Happily, she agreed that session by session she could see my confidence growing and she reassured me that I was OK and that there was a good chance that I was going to emerge from all this hell with a balanced, healthy outlook on life.

We were coming into late April now and my diagnosis would be one year old on 11 June.

Would I really be finished with all the treatment and

hospital appointments in just a few weeks? Was there any possibility that I could confront and, more importantly, conquer this horrible anniversary? I had no idea now. My previous confidence in the order of my life had been shattered.

One of the most destructive legacies that a diagnosis brings is the fracturing of your confidence. There you are, getting on with your life, pottering away, and then the outside world forces its way in and everything shifts. Once I had got my head around the illness as such, I struggled with the evidence now that we are all only a doctor's appointment away from true devastation. That day back in June, Denis could have told us anything. I could have been given the grimmest news and prognosis but, somehow, I had escaped that. Now I was realising that you never truly escape. Your faith in yourself as a responsible, mature adult who is in control of your life has been utterly shaken, and after the whirlwind of diagnosis and treatment, you are left to get on with it. But how can you? If nothing else, you have learnt that you have no power over your destiny. Yes, you can try your damnedest but, ultimately, luck is the key. That is extremely difficult to rationalise because it is not a rational notion. Anything could happen, I realised, and this made me extremely vulnerable. If you have not had this sort of earth-shattering experience, it is impossible to conceive how fragile your little world can be but I think you have to find a way to enjoy that fragility and celebrate it so that if it is threatened you know what you have lost and how hard you should fight to regain it.

Such thoughts would flit in and out of my mind as I prepared to be released back into the real world. That was how it felt. With the end of my formal treatment in sight, and my counselling completed, it seemed I was being prepared to re-enter the world. But so much had happened since I had left it that I was unsure of my place within it. That day back in June 2010, I had been separated from everyone else and quarantined, and now I was going to be readmitted as a healthy, functioning adult, with two babies and the legacy of a gruelling illness. It seemed a lot. It definitely seemed overwhelming, exhausting and yet, a bit of me wondered, a tiny bit exhilarating? Maybe this could work out and I could live happily again. Maybe a day would come when I would forget that I had once been ill and that instead I was just an ordinary mum of two small boys, like so many others.

The day finally came when my last dose of radiotherapy was administered. At this point the skin around my right breast and up to my neck was red, sore, raw and angry, just like bad sunburn, but I was assured that it was temporary. I would have to mind my skin in the future but I should be back to normal within a few weeks. The doctors confirmed to me that day that I was free to go.

On that final day, baby Ross was brought in to say hi to everyone, and as we all cooed and oohed over him, the nightmare of the previous six weeks started to float away. As we went towards the car park for the final time, I was beginning to cry. John stopped and turned to me and I collapsed into his arms, sobbing. It was the first time I had cried in weeks and he just patiently held me as I wept. I was fine, I kept howling into his shoulder. Really I was fine. He stroked my ever-growing hair and patted my back reassuringly as I soaked his shirt collar with my tears. Eventually they subsided and, once he had mopped me up, we made for the car, walking hand in hand. It was quite unreal to me.

Finally, my treatment was over. One day you are knee-deep in consultants and scan results and the next you are back in your life and it is extremely weird. People asked me how I planned to celebrate the end of treatment. I used to think I would throw a huge party but by the end of radiotherapy I just wanted peace, quiet and a night's sleep. The celebration was an extremely private matter, something that happened in my heart and mind. I was wrung out, exhausted, wrecked from the demands of treatment and minding two infants, but I had the satisfaction of knowing that, for the time being, I might have emerged a bit bruised but I wasn't totally battered.

The day after my treatment ended, our first job, as I re-entered civilian life, was to return to Donegal to the hideaway we had visited when I had been doing the practice run with my wig all those months earlier. Kim and her clan were travelling with us for the May bank holiday weekend, which would coincide with our sixth wedding anniversary, so it was bound to be a fun break. The sun shone all the way on the journey and we made it just in time for Kim and myself to sip some champagne as we watched gorgeous Kate Middleton marry her prince on the TV. I sat there throughout the hours of coverage and could not believe that this was all that was required of me that day. All I had to do was sit around and chat. No rushing around, grabbing my gown and shouting last-minute instructions as I ran (usually late) out of the door to radiotherapy. No, it was just me and my family spending time together, eating ice cream in the unseasonably hot and sunny weather. Donegal was dressed in her most splendid clothes that bank holiday weekend, and places like the Glenveagh National Park were sights of such beauty that they really helped soothe my delicate spirits. After a few days of great food and buckets of sunshine, John and I were ready to return home with our babies and start making plans for the summer. All the way home in the car we discussed endless possibilities.

Radiotherapy was over. Chemotherapy was over. Surgery was over.

Was cancer finally over? Was it really all over? And, if it was, what was going to happen next?

Chapter 27

Afterwards

What happened next was confusion.

A few days after we returned from Donegal, I was feeling a little tangled up. Even though I had read lots of helpful pamphlets that warned you about the unavoidable emotional crash once treatment finished, nothing could have prepared me for that absence in my life. For months you are consumed with your treatment, and then, suddenly, it is all over and you are told to get on with your life, but your old life has changed utterly.

An outsider would think that knowing the treatment was behind you would be a cause for great joy, and of course it is, but a small part of me dreaded what was coming next precisely because I had no idea what it was. I had been a busy full-time patient for so long, juggling appointments and medicines, that I found it hard to accept the end of the all-consuming routine.

I was back in the real world and would just have to get on with it, whatever 'it' was.

I needed to think about returning to work, for example.

The original plan had been for me to have my baby and return to my show, but that was clearly no longer an option, so all I was left with were questions. Who was I now? What did I want to do now?

I think many women can trace how motherhood changed them because their timeline is so clear cut but it was a little more complicated for me. A few months after my elder boy was born, I had been plunged into life as a cancer patient so my transition from being an individual to a mum had also coincided with my transition from healthy woman to a traumatised cancer patient. I could not separate the two experiences and I was going to have to find a new way of living that encompassed all the roles I now had to play.

From a young age, I had firmly believed that I would work right through my adult life. My mother Peigí had been a primary-school teacher, then principal of her school and she had worked until her retirement a few years ago. I had grown up in the safe, cosy suburb of Dundrum with a sister and two brothers whom I both loved and fought with in the normal way. We had all gone to Irish-language schools, made great friends there and I had spoken Irish proudly and enthusiastically all my life. My parents, particularly my mother, had managed it all brilliantly. My mother's ability to juggle was breathtaking: she had raised us four children, had a great relationship with my dad, worked full time, organised the swimming classes, Irish-language classes, recorder classes, sport trips, the Guides and Scouts and, oh, yes, even run a youth orchestra. She is a most dynamic and competent woman so I had had a fantastic role model. However, although my generation of women had been told that we really 'could have it all', I was beginning to realise that this was more complicated than the bumper-sticker-slogan energy it seemed. In a way, Peigí had 'had it all', but what was my version of that going to be? What did that phrase even mean any more and what did it mean to me?

I had studied in university and headed off down the path of a really interesting and challenging career in the media. So far so good. I'd firmly believed that women could have it all, but now I was having doubts about the very premise of this phrase 'having it all'. How come we never spoke about men 'having it all'? How come it is assumed that if they are healthy and smart, they can naturally expect fulfilling family lives twinned with guiltless career progression – and may I say, good on them. No one stopped to ask how Barack Obama was going to juggle his daughters with his busy work schedule when he was first elected president of the US. The emphasis was on his wife, Michelle, and how she was going to manage both sides of his life, and we accepted that she would have to navigate the terrain between their new blurred work and home life on behalf of her family. What was more, she was giving up her hugely successful career to do it. For most of us, the prospect of becoming president of the US is not really on our to-do list so that is an extreme example, of course. Most of us mortal souls just want peaceful, happy lives, but how do working mothers manage that successfully? We have been told that we are part of a generation of women who can grow and stretch and experience the best that life has to offer, at home and at work, and it sounds just peachy. Before I had children I had fully signed up to that treaty. Now, though, guess what? I was learning that it's complicated. I was facing turning forty soon and I had two tiny children in my care. What was my position now? How did I feel about juggling all these needs? I had waited so long for us to survive a terrible situation, and now that it was all over, we were left slightly shipwrecked and I had to make some decisions.

Where did work fit in with motherhood?

Even more importantly, where did *I* fit in with motherhood, and work? I was completely confused. I loved working and had enjoyed every minute of my broadcasting career, but what now? As I thought about it, I realised that the illness had decided I should stop working for a time.

I hadn't chosen to do that. My plan had been to return to work, until the diagnosis threw everything up in the air, so maybe it was worth considering recuperating for a while, then returning to work and just seeing how it went. Maybe I would walk back in the door and think, No, this is not for me anymore, but I decided to give it a chance rather than making unnecessary lifelong decisions just days after finishing gruelling treatment. Maybe I could make it work out and handle it all. As Nora Ephron remarked, 'Yes, you can have it all but you will have to learn to embrace the chaos.' Maybe I would give the chaos a go.

I mulled over the situation for a while and then spoke to Professor Crown about it. He advised me to relax over the summer and think about returning to work later in the year. Maybe just before Christmas, he suggested. It sounded like a good plan to me so I decided that I would try to get back into the swing of my maternity leave and pick up where I had left off when my diagnosis had exploded into our lives. I would return to normal service like any other new mother and start developing a family life that was more normal. Work matters could be discussed later.

So, I began making coffee dates with old friends and playdates with my book-club gang, and I introduced baby Ross to the world of cinema by going along to the parents-and-babies screenings in Dundrum with my friend, Katie Hannon. I quickly began to enjoy myself, just like any other new mother.

The weather helped. The sun shone right through May, and I felt my crumpled mind begin to heal a little. It also helped that Ross was sleeping through the night now so my energy levels were improving all the time. I was keen to get out into the world again, so was finally accepting invitations for dinners and drinks with friends and colleagues. For the previous twelve months, John and I had hardly left the house except for hospital appointments or family occasions so now I was enjoying mixing with my pals again.

With my social life beginning to kick in and work plans being hatched, there was now only one personal challenge left for me to face and I decided to tackle it on Monday, 23 May, coincidentally the day that President Barack Obama and Michelle came to Ireland. Before I had had Oisín, I used to run a bit. I was quite fit for a while and had enjoyed pushing myself physically and clocking up the miles in the gym. Once I got pregnant the first time, though, I had let my routine slip and was only starting to get back into going to the gym when I discovered that I was pregnant again. My exercise plans had been thwarted. Even though the gym had been torturous at times, I had really missed exercise over the last two years. Being pregnant is so physically exhausting and endless that just tying your shoelaces is an enormous challenge. Running on treadmills isn't an option. If you throw my illness into the mix, things like exercise had been pushed to the bottom of the pile so I hadn't had a run in months. Now

I was desperate to try again. The idea had been ticking in my mind for a while and now it had forced itself back to the top of the list and that was partly because of the constant reminders. There had been so many days when I was driving home from hospital and would spot someone running along, then feel a stab of envy. They looked so free. I used to stare at women joggers as they bounded along the side of the road, looking so fit and healthy. They were like an alien race to me. I was so busy, so exhausted, so consumed by getting through every crappy five-minute period that the idea of even putting on my runners and heading off for some exercise felt like a foreign land for me. I hadn't the energy, the interest or the time to put on my runners and set off. I had abandoned that physical side of my life altogether.

Over the last few weeks, though, as the ravages of treatment were subsiding, I had been dreaming of running again. In those dreams I was winning Olympic medals, of course, whereas in reality I was not sure if I would make it to the end of the road, but I was determined to try.

Imagine if I could run again some day! Imagine if I wasn't pregnant and bloated from medication and I could simply put on my runners and announce cheerily that I was off for a run and it wouldn't cause panic or a flurry of phone calls. The previous year, in the blink of an eye, I had gone from being a healthy young woman to someone who could not make it safely to Dundrum Town Centre, minutes from my front door, because I was so physically vulnerable. The woman who used to just head out of the door was a stranger to me, but once radiotherapy had ended, I began to think about her again. Maybe I could reclaim her. I decided it was worth a shot.

So, one bright and very breezy Monday morning, the day the Obamas were due in town, I quietly put on my tracksuit, packed my runners into a bag and went out. I didn't tell anyone except John what my plans were, just said I would be back in an hour.

I clambered into the car, turned on the engine and my heart started beating a little faster. I headed off towards Marlay Park, a huge and gorgeous woodland with rolling fields near my home. As I drove along I suddenly noticed that I was singing to some tune on the radio. My hand was lightly tapping on the steering wheel. I realised I was thinking about lunch or dinner, something mundane like that. The point was, I was not thinking about cancer. Or treatment. Or appointments or lifts to the hospital. I was driving myself, without the whole world being involved, up to a park for a run and it felt great.

I made my way through the familiar gates and swung my car into an empty space. I turned off the engine and swapped my shoes for my dusty runners, then hopped out, leaning against the car door to do a couple of warm-up stretches before I walked towards the path that loops its way around Marlay's vast green spaces.

I know that park extremely well. I had been visiting it since I was a child and one of my most cherished memories was bringing Oisín there for the first time when he was just a few weeks old. Eighteen months later, he had taken his first steps at the playground so it was really sacred ground for me.

As these thoughts started going around in my mind, I began walking slightly faster, building up a little speed. I was following the path around the perimeter of the park and asking myself, am I really going to do this? I tried to concentrate on my feet and empty my mind of all the images and half-memories that were floating around from the previous year.

Look up to the Dublin Mountains and let them inspire you, I ordered myself, and so they did.

Then I passed some familiar landmarks: the little bridge across the stream, the bright white goalposts stretching as high as the trees, the large oak I had played under many times as a child. As I drank it all in, I could feel my pace quicken. My hesitant steps had begun to speed up and then it happened. My body took over and started to push itself.

I was running.

Yes, it was more stumbling than racing, but it didn't matter. I definitely seemed to be running. The wind rushed through my hair in a way that only happens when you are moving at a pace. I nervously placed one foot after the other and somehow kept going. I'm sure I looked completely unfit and awkward to passers-by as I galloped clumsily along but I didn't care. It felt amazing.

Running.

Me running.

And while I was certainly the most graceless athlete in the park that morning, I can also guarantee that I was the happiest. Hooray, I was running. I was doing it badly but running all the same.

'I can run, I can move,' I shouted up at the sky, and then the tears rolled down my cheeks as I ploughed on, but this time I didn't mind them.

'Look, I'm ACTUALLY RUNNING!' I yelled to the trees, as I stumbled along. The wind picked up and helped drive me along and I was happy. And then little whispers of thoughts began to blossom in my mind.

If I could finally do this, maybe, just maybe, it could be OK again.

Maybe, just maybe, I could live a life again.

Maybe, just maybe, this part of our story was finally over and we could confidently face into whatever was next for us and our boys.

Maybe.

Just maybe, Ross.

Epilogue

New Year's Eve, 2013

Dear Ross,

A few weeks ago, I had a wonderful phone call from Denis Evoy's office and the conversation went like this.

Me (anxiously): Hello?

Them: Your results are clear. The mammogram is clear.

Me (loud exhale): Thanks ... thanks so much ... I kind of knew that it was fine but it's great to get the call, thanks so much. Thanks.

Them: Evelyn, you're very welcome.

Then ...

Them: See you in a year.

Me (stumbling): Great. Thanks. Yes, in a year. See you in a year's time.

Click.

Rossy, it's over three years since the nightmare began, and I have had my third clear annual mammogram and life is now good.

You are great, Daddy is wonderful and Oisín is really enjoying his new life in *naíonra* pre-school. You are lined up to go there next year.

You are a chatty, adventurous little boy, who turns three in just a few weeks' time, and you hug, then tussle with your brother just like any normal siblings. Happily, you seem to be the best of friends.

Life in work is busy too. When you were turning a year old, I returned to work at my old stomping ground in RTÉ Radio. Earlier in the week, I was even presenting a live radio show, so that part of my working life, which I feared had evaporated for ever, has kicked right back in again, which is truly lovely. When I nervously walked back into the radio centre that first day after everything, it immediately felt familiar and great to be there, so I am now juggling on a grand scale as I work and look after you guys, but I think we're all doing really well. You all seem happy and we blunder through in nice, organised chaos.

When I'm in work, I still miss himself, though, and often when I pass our old Gerry Ryan Show studio, I wink at the photo of Gerry that hangs outside.

In terms of my health, I feel really well and there are many days when I don't even think about the diagnosis and the nightmare we endured. At the same time, though, I know that the whole experience has definitely changed me in a thousand different little ways.

First, it has made me feel lucky. On 11 June 2010, I thought I would slip into an abyss of pain and worry, but three years later I feel lucky because I recovered and got to live again.

I also learnt that the words we use around cancer are wrong. *I* did not battle cancer, and *I* certainly did not win against it. The medical teams do that. I was just lucky that mine was a treatable form. I believe now that the only battle cancer forces you to have is with yourself. It makes you fight like a dog to grasp some shred of control, some scrap of dignity and calm in the middle of a most terrifying situation. A diagnosis sends you to war with yourself as you struggle against the darkness that descends all around you. Trying to emerge from it happy and confident is the battle. The rest is up to the medics and you cannot control that. You just have to hope that you are lucky.

And I was lucky, but there are some little traces of the whole experience, though. Sometimes I have a swollen right hand on the side where my lymph nodes were removed, and I stare at it as I massage the skin and then I forget about it.

Occasionally I look at my breast in the mirror and wonder how that fading amazing scar could have caused so much trauma, but then you or your brother calls, reminding me to hurry up and get on with it. I finish dressing and move on.

I only see my doctors once a year now and my annual mammograms have always been clear so that intensive medical part of the experience has quietly faded away.

I take Tamoxifen daily to regulate my oestrogen levels, and the side effects, while mildly irritating at times, are a small price to pay for the reassurance it offers.

In terms of cancer, I am now convinced that much more money should be invested in researching this vicious disease in all its forms. Clinical research is the key to unlocking the horrendous grip that cancer has over patients, so I am very proud to be a patient advocate for a charity called ICORG (the All Ireland Cooperative Clinical Research Group), which focuses on research and trials. It was originally set up by Professor John Crown, among others, and he often asks about you when I run into him at meetings!

The charity does extraordinary work, pioneering treatment trials here in Ireland, but there is so much more to do. I am passionate about the work that ICORG could deliver with more funding, so we need money. Yes, be warned, you will be bored rigid listening to me talk about cancer research over the following years, I suspect, but maybe some day you and your brother will jump out of a plane or some such to raise money for it!

So, what else? Well, we still go to Kerry on our holidays and have booked to go again next August. I know you'll find it exciting that so many of your cousins will be there for you to play with on the beach, and Daddy and I are already looking forward to seeing you enjoy swimming in the sea!

We have so many plans for you both, and life is clearly a bit busy with a three- and a four-year-old in the house but, most importantly, it is normal, and that is all that we ever wanted. Lovely, sweet normal. Tonight we put you and Oisín to bed, pretending to you both that we would wake you up at midnight to see in the new year, but I think it will be just Daddy and me, sitting by the fire, quietly welcoming in 2014 at midnight. We will toast each other and breathe a sigh of relief that this change of date pushes our whole nightmare even further away from us. We may even smile at each other, and we will celebrate the fact that we are there, cocooned in our little boys' world, safe in the knowledge that we have seen the worst that life can throw at us and somehow, with all the love and support in the world, we came through it together. That will be enough to celebrate, I think.

With that in mind, it is probably time for me to go and put on another wash (there is always another wash!), but before I go, let me end with this.

You and Oisín are the centre of Daddy's and my world. We love both of you so much and count ourselves so lucky that you came along when you did.

And always know this: even when I read back to all the horror we endured in those months during the pregnancy, I would do it all again for you.

All of it.

Every minute of it.

Yes, I would do it all.

In a heartbeat.

For your heartbeat.

Love,

Mama

Acknowledgements

The word acknowledgement seems too thin for the weight of thanks this section has to carry, but how else to explain the depth of my gratitude to people who held my hand when I needed it most?

Best to start at the beginning.

Do mo mháthair Peigí. Mo bhuíochas síoraí duit as do ghrá agus do thacaíocht, go mór mhór as an aire a thugann tú do mo bhuachaillí beaga. You are our favourite breakfast visitor! And though we all still miss darling Dad Pascal, I know he would have been so proud of the family and how we all look after each other in good times and bad as demonstrated on these pages.

My sister Kim. You walked with us every step of the way, regardless of how dark and treacherous the road became at times. Grá mór. My wonderful brothers Brian and Colm – my rocks in an uncertain world – deepest thanks to you both. I have to also thank my siblings for marrying such wonderful people, Norman Fitzgerald, Maria Hadjitheodosiou O'Rourke and Anita O'Rourke – you were all amazingly supportive of us.

Luckily when I married John, I gained a wonderful extended clan with my mother and father-in-law Margaret and Brian McMahon. Every time we needed help, whether we even knew it or not, you were always there to carry us. I am the luckiest DIL. And my list of lovely relatives doesn't end there as John's brothers, Brian and Evin and their wives Sue and Claire are always wonderfully supportive of us. I particularly want to acknowledge Brian's cheery texts particularly on chemotherapy days – repeat after me, blue chairs are for winners, brown chairs for losers.

Back in 2010, I dreaded walking in that first day to St Vincent's Hospital but if I had known the army of extraordinarily impressive, compassionate and talented medics I would meet there, my step would have been lighter. My thanks to Dr Laura Barker from the Leopardstown Women's Medical Clinic who sent me to St Vincent's at the very beginning. Huge thanks to the breast-care nurses I met there, Clare Glenane, Grainne Griffin and Mary Kieran who could not have been kinder to myself and John. My heartfelt thanks to my brilliant surgeon Mr Denis Evoy and his wife Kitty, whose unwavering interest and support was always so important to us. Dr Ann O'Doherty was the best ally a patient could hope to meet. Thank you, Ann. I find it nearly impossible to describe how important my oncologist Professor John Crown has been in our lives. He guided us through a nightmare with his amazing skill and experience and we are indebted to him for minding myself and Ross so incredibly well throughout. Thanks to all the kindness shown to us by the nursing and other medical staff in St Vincent's Hospital. My thanks also to Professor John Armstrong and his team at the Beacon Hospital for their wonderful care during my radiotherapy treatment. Another professor with a tough assignment was our obstetrician in Holles Street, Prof. Fionnuala McAuliffe, who monitored my pregnancy so carefully and delivered our beautiful baby boy to us in February 2011. Sincere thanks to her and all the incredible nursing staff at NMH Holles Street. While I'm thanking hospital staff, a word of gratitude to all those who minded Ross in Our Lady's Children's Hospital, Crumlin when he was just five weeks old.

To my forever friends gathered during my school, college and Galway adventures, Emer Conlon, Elayne Devlin, Michael Connolly, Emma McIvor, Michael Parke, Michael Cregan, Gretta Manners, Aedin Gormley, Mary McAuliffe, Marie Louise Coolahan, Deirdre Healy, Clodagh Browne, Deirdre O'Connor, Deborah Wiseman, Rory O'Connell, Niall Mooney and Grainne Lynch –

thanks for the endless lunches, phone calls and cups of tea. Also thanks to our lovely next-door neighbours on the other side, Deirdre and Patrick Phelan, for the cheery chats over the wall.

Thanks to Celine Curtin, who always keeps a close eye on us from her Galway HQ. What can I say about Mariana Araujo, our fantastic nanny? You swept into our lives at a dark moment, and the love and care you showered on our two boys lifted me on many a day. My aunty Eileen Roche, thanks for the love you beamed to us from Moyvane in Kerry. Huge thanks too to Lindsey Holmes for her friendship and professional help.

And now to the amazing friends and colleagues I have gathered over the years in RTÉ. I am so grateful for the countless cards and letters that many colleagues sent and every good wish helped. I want to thank in particular Ann Marie Power, Anne Farrell, Alice O'Sullivan, Katie Hannon, Joe Hoban, Andrew Fitzpatrick, Eithne Hand, Philip Boucher-Hayes for his free advice (it is, isn't it? #anxious), Ryan Tubridy, who went as far as to agree to launch this book, Sian O'Gorman, who was so supportive when I first whispered to her that I was thinking of maybe writing a book, Sinead Egan, Sandra Byrne, JP Coakley and Annette Malone, who was endlessly helpful to myself and John, while also badgering me to do this. Thanks in particular to my colleagues on *Arena*, Sean Rocks, Sinead Mooney, Penny Hart, Derek Nagle and Abie Philbin Bowman. Deep gratitude to *Arena*'s series producer

Nuala O'Neill, who welcomed me back so warmly to the radio world. A special word of thanks to the *Gerry Ryan Show* team, Siobhan Hough, Deirdre Magee, Brenda Donohue, Lorraine Dunne, Louise Ní Chríodáin, Fiona Murray, Helen Howard, John Bela Reilly, Eileen Heron and Therese Kelly – they told us and we told them. To my radio bosses in RTÉ who were so sympathetic throughout my illness. I want to especially thank Lorelei Harris, Tom McGuire and Director of Radio, Jim Jennings who have been so encouraging as I prepare to launch this story into the big bad world. Another radio friend is the *Gerry Ryan Show* listener Brigid Mulqueen who reached out to me at the exact moment I needed it, so love and thanks to her and her precious son Jack. Brigid, I am so grateful you sent that email that day. Sincere thanks too to Morah, Mike and the Ryan family for their interest and support in this book.

Thanks also to the early readers for their great advice, Paula Mulroe and Emma Dunne. Huge thanks to the volunteers at the ARC drop-in cancer support centre, you serve the best tea in Dublin! Every month for the past eight years, my heart lifts when I know it is book club night, so endless gratitude to my bookish pals, Louise Barr, Moira Moloney and Louise Regan, your chocolate cakes have sustained me for years now.

GRMA to our 'nearly' cousins, the Farley family. In particular I want to thank the lovely Aoileann Farley who has always been there for us. Huge thanks too to Jane,

Fidelma and Tom Farley and all their crew who make the annual pilgrimage to Kerry such a joy. Heartfelt thanks to our Kells Bay friends, especially the fabulous Mary Kavanagh, whose generosity allowed our family to have a badly needed holiday in summer 2010. The kindness you showed us will always stay with me.

And now to the book. Profound thanks to my incredible agent Marianne Gunn O'Connor. Marianne, you will never know how important that first magical 'yes, I want more' message was to me. Her confidence in the appeal of the book was inspiring. I am thrilled to be publishing *Dear Ross* with Hachette Ireland. I still can't quite believe it is happening! The endless guidance and support my editor Ciara Doorley has given me to untangle this knotty tale has been terrific. Thanks so much, Ciara. Deepest thanks also to all the team at Hachette involved in the production of this book.

Finally, our nieces, nephews and god children – you made us believe that it would all be worth it because of the love and fun you have brought us over the years. In order of age, Daniel, Lia, Kate, Oscar, Zenon, Conor, Eden, Dylan, Leda, John, Max and Lucy xx